1986
YEARBOOK
OF ASTRONOMY

edited by
Patrick Moore

1986 YEARBOOK OF ASTRONOMY

edited by
Patrick Moore

Sidgwick & Jackson Limited
LONDON

First Published in Great Britain 1985

Copyright © 1985 by Sidgwick and Jackson Limited

Published in Great Britain by
Sidgwick & Jackson Limited
1 Tavistock Chambers, Bloomsbury Way
London WC1A 2SG

0–283–99263–8 (HARD)
0–283–99264–6 (LIMP)

Printed in Great Britain by
Biddles Ltd, Guildford, Surrey

Contents

Part Two: *Article Section*

Part Three: *Miscellaneous*

Editor's Foreword

1986 is a momentous year in astronomy. Halley's Comet passes perihelion; the Giotto space-probe is scheduled to pass through it in March; in January, Voyager 2 makes its rendezvous with the planet Uranus; the new William Herschel telescope should come into operation in La Palma, and we may expect major developments in space research.

Obviously, this issue of the *Yearbook* is dominated to some extent by Halley's Comet, but – as usual I have tried to include something of interest for everybody, with articles ranging from the Solar System out to remote galaxies, and at various technical levels. I hope that the result will be acceptable. As usual, we are indebted to Gordon Taylor for the Monthly Notes on phenomena; without him, it would indeed have been difficult to produce this latest issue. We must also give grateful thanks to all our contributors, old and new.

PATRICK MOORE

Selsey, May 1985

Preface

New readers will find that all the information in this *Yearbook* is given in diagrammatic or descriptive form; the positions of the planets may easily be found on the specially designed star charts, while the monthly notes describe the movements of the planets and give details of other astronomical phenomena visible in both the northern and southern hemisphere. Two sets of star charts are provided. The **Northern Charts** (pp. 14 to 39) are designed for use in latitude 52 degrees north, but may be used without alteration throughout the British Isles, and (except in the case of eclipses and occultations) in other countries of similar north latitude. The **Southern Charts** (pp. 40 to 65) are drawn for latitude 35 degrees south, and are suitable for use in South Africa, Australia and New Zealand, and other stations in approximately the same south latitude. The reader who needs more detailed information will find *Norton's Star Atlas* (Gall and Inglis) an invaluable guide, while more precise positions of the planets and their satellites, together with predictions of occultations, meteor showers, and periodic comets may be found in the *Handbook* of the British Astronomical Association. A somewhat similar publication is the *Observer's Handbook* of the Royal Astronomical Society of Canada, and readers will also find details of forthcoming events given in the American *Sky and Telescope*. This monthly publication also produces a special occultation supplement giving predictions for the United States and Canada.

Important Note
 The times given on the star charts and in the Monthly Notes are generally given as local times, using the 24-hour clock, the day beginning at midnight. All the dates, and the times of a few events (e.g. eclipses), are given in Greenwich Mean Time (G.M.T.), which is related to local time by the formula

Local Mean Time = G.M.T. – west longitude.

In practice, small differences of longitudes are ignored, and the observer will use local clock time, which will be the appropriate Standard (or Zone) Time. As the formula indicates, places in west longitude will have a Standard Time slow on G.M.T., while places in east longitude will have Standard Time fast on G.M.T. As examples we have:

Standard Time in

New Zealand	G.M.T.	+	12 hours
Victoria; N.S.W.	G.M.T.	+	10 hours
Western Australia	G.M.T.	+	8 hours
South Africa	G.M.T.	+	2 hours
British Isles	G.M.T.		
Eastern S.T.	G.M.T.	−	5 hours
Central S.T.	G.M.T.	−	6 hours, etc

If Summer Time is in use, the clocks will have been advanced by one hour, and this hour must be subtracted from the clock time to give Standard Time.

Due to the procrastination by the British Government the dates of Summer Time are still undecided at the time of going to press!

In Great Britain and N. Ireland, Summer Time may be in force in 1986 from March $30^d 01^h$ until October $26^d 01^h$ G.M.T.

PART ONE

Monthly Charts and Astronomical Phenomena

Notes on the Star Charts

The stars, together with the Sun, Moon and planets seem to be set on the surface of the celestial sphere, which appears to rotate about the Earth from east to west. Since it is impossible to represent a curved surface accurately on a plane, any kind of star map is bound to contain some form of distortion. But it is well known that the eye can endure some kinds of distortion better than others, and it is particularly true that the eye is most sensitive to deviations from the vertical and horizontal. For this reason the star charts given in this volume have been designed to give a true representation of vertical and horizontal lines, whatever may be the resulting distortion in the shape of a constellation figure. It will be found that the amount of distortion is, in general, quite small, and is only obvious in the case of large constellations such as Leo and Pegasus, when these appear at the top of the charts, and so are drawn out sideways.

The charts show all stars down to the fourth magnitude, together with a number of fainter stars which are necessary to define the shape of a constellation. There is no standard system for representing the outlines of the constellations, and triangles and other simple figures have been used to give outlines which are easy to follow with the naked eye. The names of the constellations are given, together with the proper names of the brighter stars. The apparent magnitudes of the stars are indicated roughly by using four different sizes of dots, the larger dots representing the bright stars.

The two sets of star charts are similar in design. At each opening there is a group of four charts which give a complete coverage of the sky up to an altitude of 62½ degrees; there are twelve such groups to cover the entire year. In the **Northern Charts** (for 52 degrees north) the upper two charts show the southern sky, south being at the centre and east on the left. The coverage is from 10 degrees north of east (top left) to 10 degrees north of west (top right). The two lower charts show the northern sky from 10 degrees south of west (lower left) to 10 degrees south of east (lower right). There is thus an overlap east and west.

Conversely, in the **Southern Charts** (for 35 degrees south) the upper two charts show the northern sky, with north at the centre and east on the right. The two lower charts show the southern sky, with south at the centre and east on the left. The coverage and overlap is the same on both sets of charts.

Because the sidereal day is shorter than the solar day, the stars appear to rise and set about four minutes earlier each day, and this amounts to two hours in a month. Hence the twelve groups of charts in each set are sufficient to give the appearance of the sky throughout the day at intervals of two hours, or at the same time of night at monthly intervals throughout the year. The actual range of dates and times when the stars on the charts are visible is indicated at the top of each page. Each group is numbered in bold type, and the number to be used for any given month and time is summarized in the following table:

Local Time	18h	20h	22h	0h	2h	4h	6h
January	11	12	1	2	3	4	5
February	12	1	2	3	4	5	6
March	1	2	3	4	5	6	7
April	2	3	4	5	6	7	8
May	3	4	5	6	7	8	9
June	4	5	6	7	8	9	10
July	5	6	7	8	9	10	11
August	6	7	8	9	10	11	12
September	7	8	9	10	11	12	1
October	8	9	10	11	12	1	2
November	9	10	11	12	1	2	3
December	10	11	12	1	2	3	4

The charts are drawn to scale, the horizontal measurements, marked at every 10 degrees, giving the azimuths (or true bearings) measured from the north round through east (90 degrees), south (180 degrees), and west (270 degrees). The vertical measurements, similarly marked, give the altitudes of the stars up to 62½ degrees. Estimates of altitude and azimuth made from these charts will necessarily be mere approximations, since no observer will be exactly at the adopted latitude, or at the stated time, but they will serve for the identification of stars and planets.

The ecliptic is drawn as a broken line on which longitude is marked at every 10 degrees; the positions of the planets are then easily found by reference to the table of page 72. It will be noticed that on the Southern Charts the ecliptic may reach an altitude in excess of 62½ degrees on star charts 5 to 9. The continuation of the broken line will be found on the charts of overhead stars.

There is a curious illusion that stars at an altitude of 60 degrees or more are actually overhead, and the beginner may often feel that he is leaning over backwards in trying to see them. These overhead stars are given spearately on the pages immediately following the main star charts. The entire year is covred at one opening, each of the four maps showing the overhead stars at times which corespond to those of three of the main star charts. The position of the zenith is indicated by a cross, and this cross marks the centre of a circle which is 35 degrees from the zenith; there s thus a small overlap with the main charts.

The broken line leading from the north (on the Northern Charts) or from the south (on the Southern Charts) is numbered to indicate the corresponding main chart. Thus on page 38 the N-S line numbered 6 is to be regarded as an extension of the centre (south) linc of chart 6 on pages 24 and 25, and at the top of these pages are printed the dates and times which are appropriate. Similarly, on page 65, the S-N line numbered 10 connects with the north line of the upper charts on pages 58 and 59.

The overhead stars are plotted as maps on a conical projection, and the scale is rather smaller than that of the main charts.

1L

October 6 at 5^h October 21 at 4^h
November 6 at 3^h November 21 at 2^h
December 6 at 1^h December 21 at midnight
January 6 at 23^h January 21 at 22^h
February 6 at 21^h February 21 at 20^h

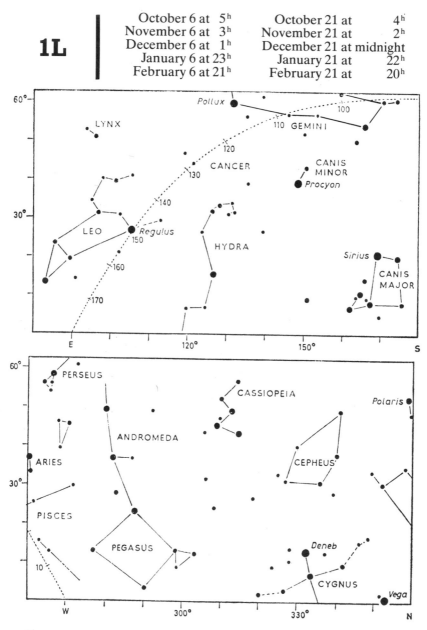

October 6 at 5ʰ   October 21 at   4ʰ
November 6 at 3ʰ   November 21 at   2ʰ
December 6 at 1ʰ   December 21 at midnight
January 6 at 23ʰ   January 21 at   22ʰ
February 6 at 21ʰ   February 21 at   20ʰ

1R

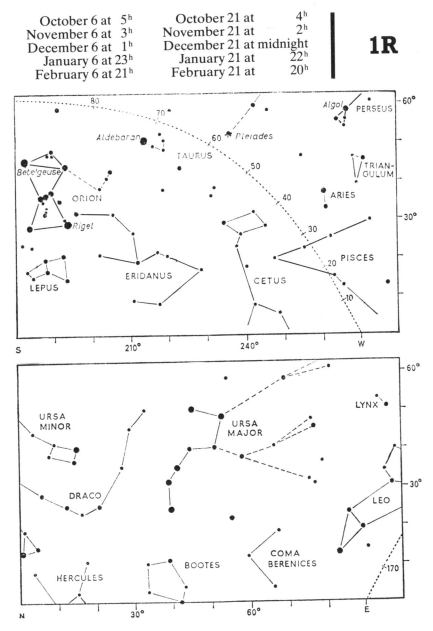

2L

November 6 at 5ʰ
December 6 at 3ʰ
January 6 at 1ʰ
February 6 at 23ʰ
March 6 at 21ʰ

November 21 at 4ʰ
December 21 at 2ʰ
January 21 at midnight
February 21 at 22ʰ
March 21 at 20ʰ

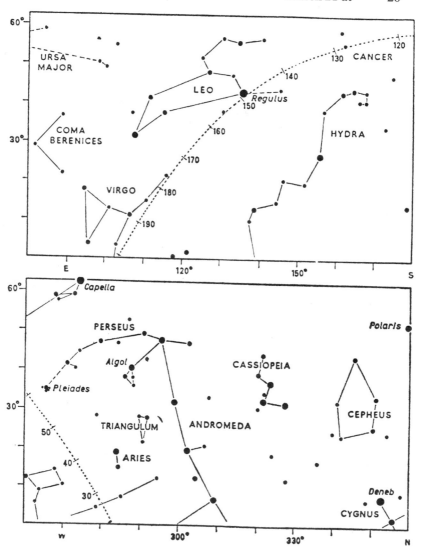

November 6 at 5ʰ	November 21 at	4ʰ
December 6 at 3ʰ	December 21 at	2ʰ
January 6 at 1ʰ	January 21 at midnight	
February 6 at 23ʰ	February 21 at	22ʰ
March 6 at 21ʰ	March 21 at	20ʰ

2R

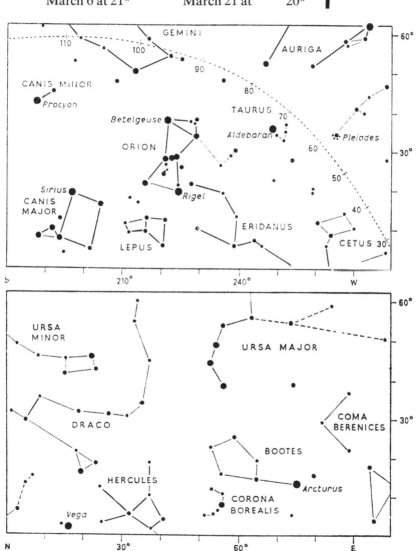

3L

December 6 at 5^h December 21 at 4^h
January 6 at 3^h January 21 at 2^h
February 6 at 1^h February 21 at midnight
March 6 at 23^h March 21 at 22^h
April 6 at 21^h April 21 at 20^h

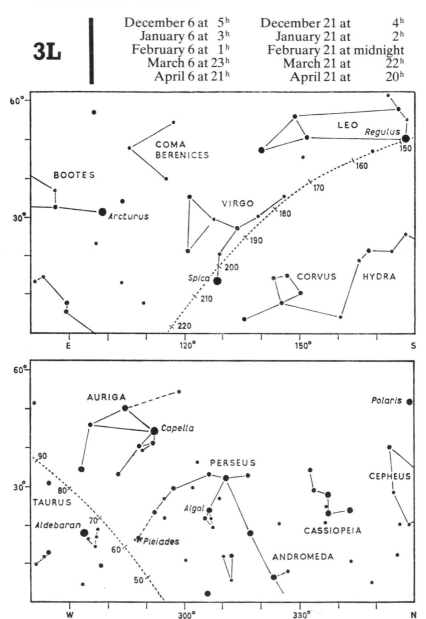

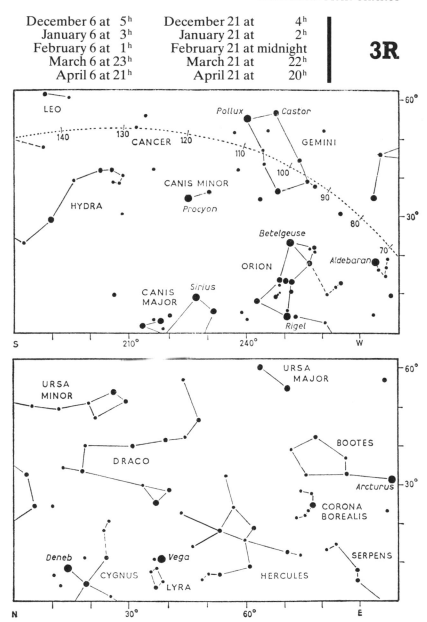

December 6 at 5ʰ	December 21 at 4ʰ
January 6 at 3ʰ	January 21 at 2ʰ
February 6 at 1ʰ	February 21 at midnight
March 6 at 23ʰ	March 21 at 22ʰ
April 6 at 21ʰ	April 21 at 20ʰ

3R

LEO

Pollux • Castor

140 130 CANCER 120 GEMINI

110

CANIS MINOR 100

HYDRA *Procyon* 90

80

Betelgeuse

70

ORION *Aldebaran*

CANIS *Sirius*
MAJOR

Rigel

S 210° 240° W

URSA URSA
MINOR MAJOR

BOOTES

DRACO

Arcturus

CORONA
BOREALIS

Deneb *Vega* SERPENS

CYGNUS HERCULES

LYRA

N 30° 60° E

19

4L

January 6 at 5ʰ	January 21 at 4ʰ
February 6 at 3ʰ	February 21 at 2ʰ
March 6 at 1ʰ	March 21 at midnight
April 6 at 23ʰ	April 21 at 22ʰ
May 6 at 21ʰ	May 21 at 20ʰ

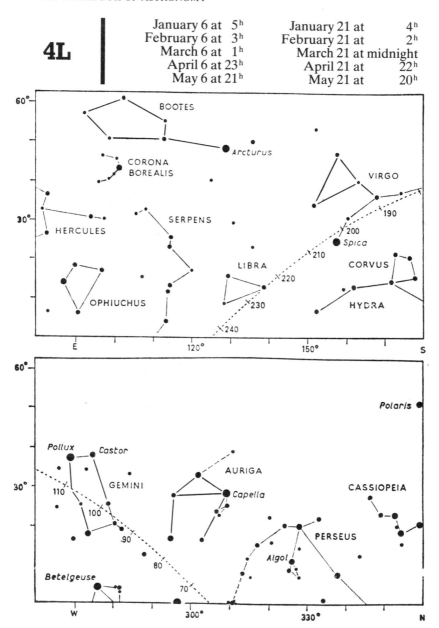

January 6 at   5ʰ   January 21 at   4ʰ
February 6 at   3ʰ   February 21 at   2ʰ
March 6 at   1ʰ   March 21 at midnight   **4R**
April 6 at 23ʰ   April 21 at   22ʰ
May 6 at 21ʰ   May 21 at   20ʰ

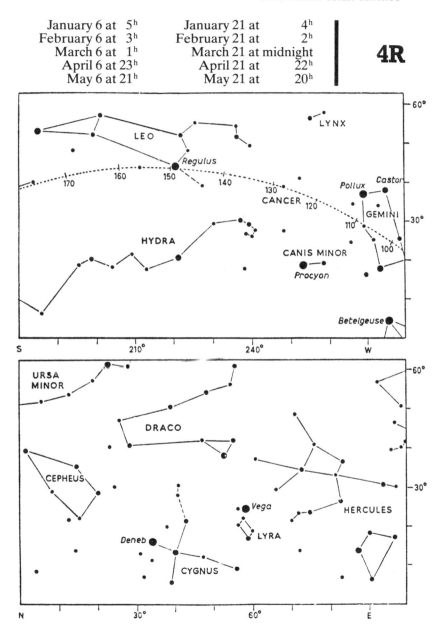

21

5L

January 6 at 7ʰ	January 21 at 6ʰ
February 6 at 5ʰ	February 21 at 4ʰ
March 6 at 3ʰ	March 21 at 2ʰ
April 6 at 1ʰ	April 21 at midnight
May 6 at 23ʰ	May 21 at 22ʰ

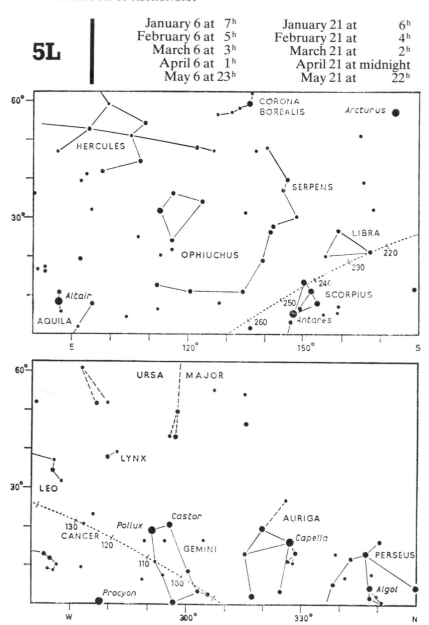

January 6 at 7^h	January 21 at 6^h
February 6 at 5^h	February 21 at 4^h
March 6 at 3^h	March 21 at 2^h
April 6 at 1^h	April 21 at midnight
May 6 at 23^h	May 21 at 22^h

5R

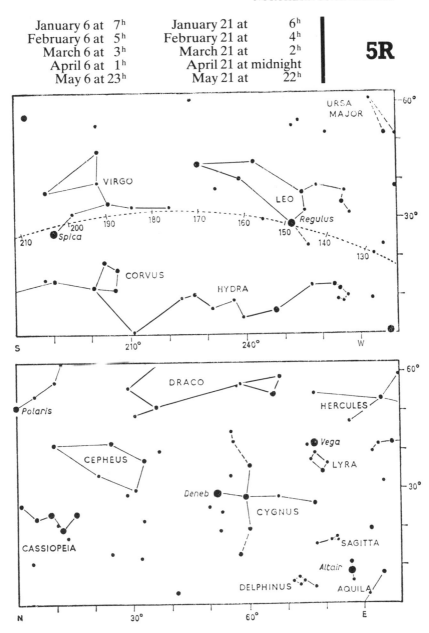

6L

March 6 at 5ʰ	March 21 at 4ʰ
April 6 at 3ʰ	April 21 at 2ʰ
May 6 at 1ʰ	May 21 at midnight
June 6 at 23ʰ	June 21 at 22ʰ
July 6 at 21ʰ	July 21 at 20ʰ

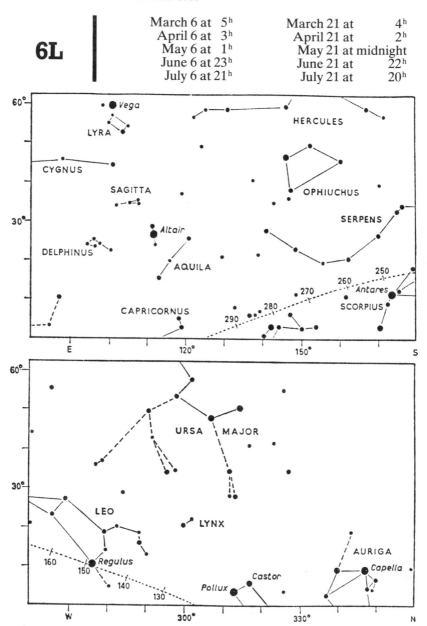

March 6 at	5ʰ	March 21 at	4ʰ
April 6 at	3ʰ	April 21 at	2ʰ
May 6 at	1ʰ	May 21 at midnight	
June 6 at 23ʰ		June 21 at	22ʰ
July 6 at 21ʰ		July 21 at	20ʰ

6R

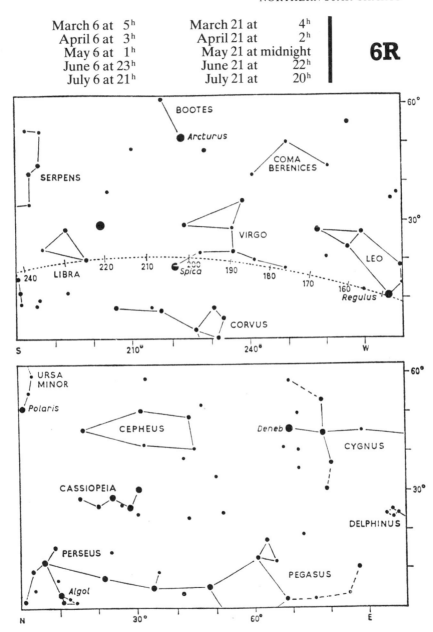

7L

May 6 at 3^h
June 6 at 1^h
July 6 at 23^h
August 6 at 21^h
September 6 at 19^h

May 21 at   2^h
June 21 at midnight
July 21 at   22^h
August 21 at   20^h
September 21 at   18^h

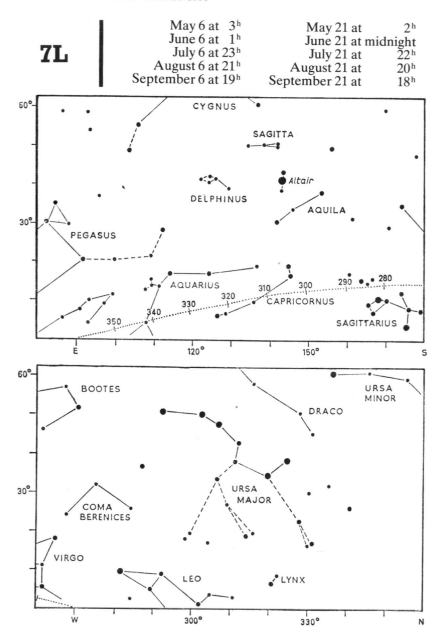

May 6 at 3ʰ   May 21 at   2ʰ
June 6 at 1ʰ   June 21 at midnight
July 6 at 23ʰ   July 21 at   22ʰ   **7R**
August 6 at 21ʰ   August 21 at   20ʰ
September 6 at 19ʰ   September 21 at   18ʰ

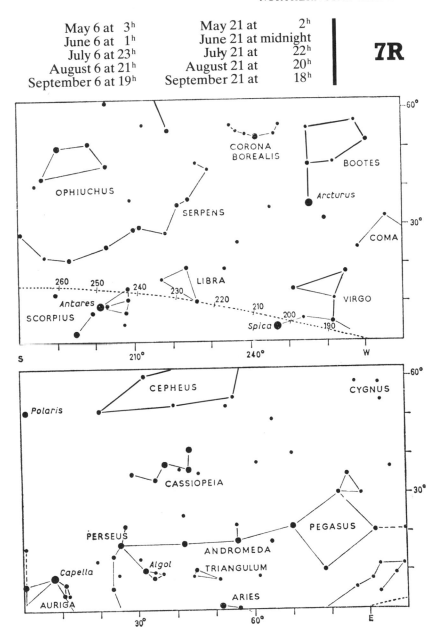

8L

July 6 at 1ʰ	July 21 at midnight
August 6 at 23ʰ	August 21 at 22ʰ
September 6 at 21ʰ	September 21 at 20ʰ
October 6 at 19ʰ	October 21 at 18ʰ
November 6 at 17ʰ	November 21 at 16ʰ

July 6 at 1ʰ	July 21 at midnight
August 6 at 23ʰ	August 21 at 22ʰ
September 6 at 21ʰ	September 21 at 20ʰ
October 6 at 19ʰ	October 21 at 18ʰ
November 6 at 17ʰ	November 21 at 16ʰ

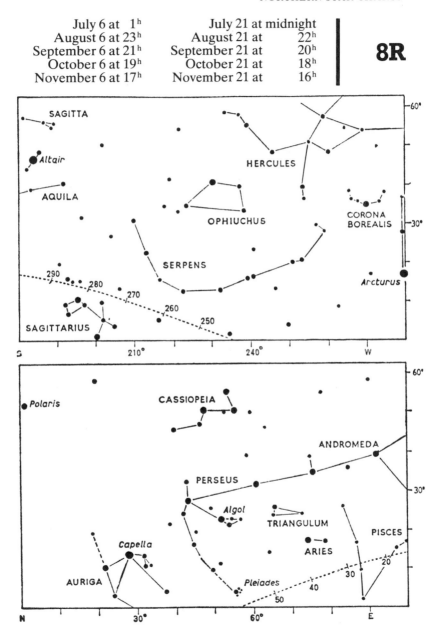

29

9L

August 6 at 1ʰ	August 21 at midnight
September 6 at 23ʰ	September 21 at 22ʰ
October 6 at 21ʰ	October 21 at 20ʰ
November 6 at 19ʰ	November 21 at 18ʰ
December 6 at 17ʰ	December 21 at 16ʰ

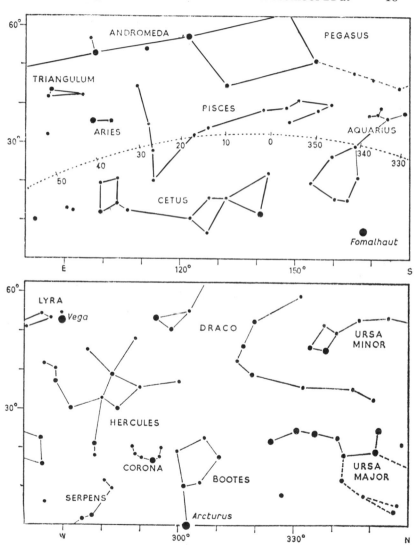

August 6 at 1ʰ August 21 at midnight
September 6 at 23ʰ September 21 at 22ʰ
October 6 at 21ʰ October 21 at 20ʰ
November 6 at 19ʰ November 21 at 18ʰ
December 6 at 17ʰ December 21 at 16ʰ

9R

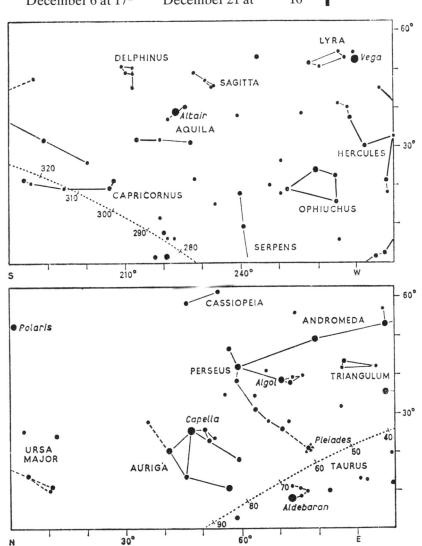

11L

September 6 at 3ʰ
October 6 at 1ʰ
November 6 at 23ʰ
December 6 at 21ʰ
January 6 at 19ʰ

September 21 at 2ʰ
October 21 at midnight
November 21 at 22ʰ
December 21 at 20ʰ
January 21 at 18ʰ

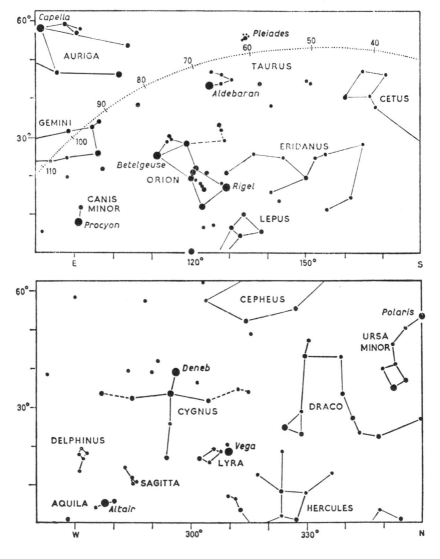

September 6 at 3ʰ   September 21 at   2ʰ
October 6 at 1ʰ   October 21 at midnight
November 6 at 23ʰ   November 21 at   22ʰ   **11R**
December 6 at 21ʰ   December 21 at   20ʰ
January 6 at 19ʰ   January 21 at   18ʰ

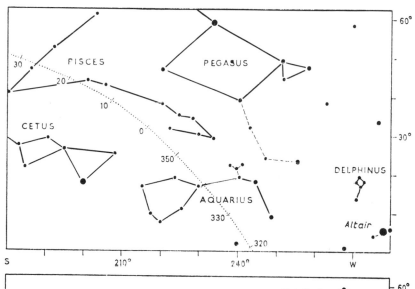

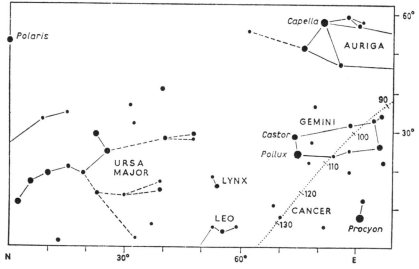

12L

October 6 at 3ʰ	October 21 at 2ʰ
November 6 at 1ʰ	November 21 at midnight
December 6 at 23ʰ	December 21 at 22ʰ
January 6 at 21ʰ	January 21 at 20ʰ
February 6 at 19ʰ	February 21 at 18ʰ

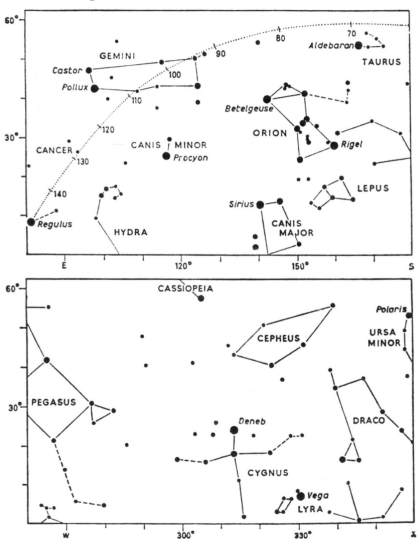

October 6 at   3ʰ
November 6 at   1ʰ
December 6 at 23ʰ
January 6 at 21ʰ
February 6 at 19ʰ

October 21 at   2ʰ
November 21 at midnight
December 21 at   22ʰ
January 21 at   20ʰ
February 21 at   18ʰ

12R

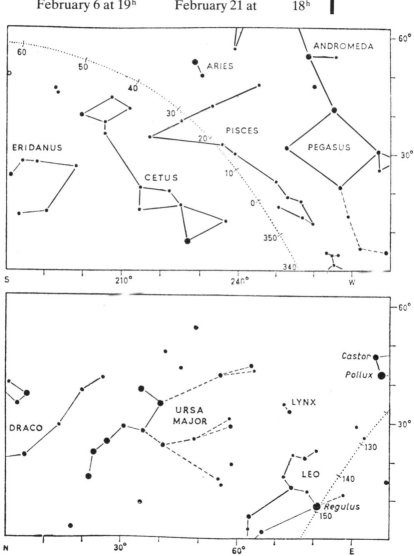

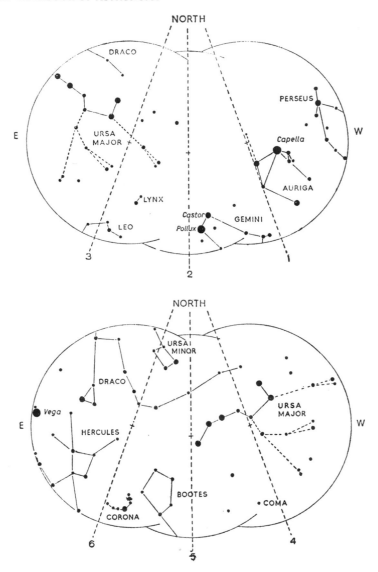

Northern Hemisphere Overhead Stars

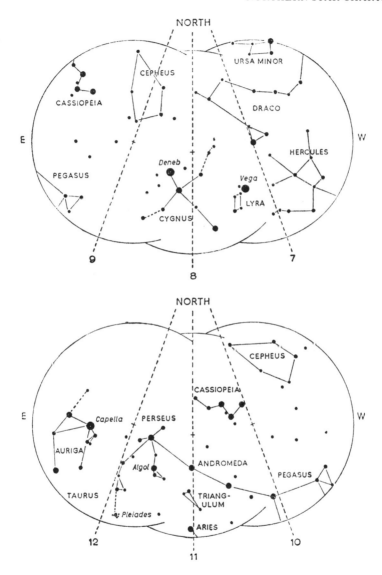

NORTH

URSA MINOR

CEPHEUS

CASSIOPEIA

DRACO

E

W

HERCULES

Deneb

PEGASUS

Vega

LYRA

CYGNUS

9

8

7

NORTH

CEPHEUS

CASSIOPEIA

E

W

Capella PERSEUS

AURIGA

ANDROMEDA

Algol

PEGASUS

TAURUS

TRIANG-
ULUM

Pleiades

ARIES

12

11

10

Northern Hemisphere Overhead Stars

39

1L

October 6 at 5^h October 21 at 4^h
November 6 at 3^h November 21 at 2^h
December 6 at 1^h December 21 at midnight
January 6 at 23^h January 21 at 22^h
February 6 at 21^h February 21 at 20^h

October 6 at 5ʰ   October 21 at   4ʰ
November 6 at 3ʰ   November 21 at   2ʰ
December 6 at 1ʰ   December 21 at midnight
January 6 at 23ʰ   January 21 at   22ʰ
February 6 at 21ʰ   February 21 at   20ʰ

1R

2L

November 6 at 5^h November 21 at   4^h
December 6 at 3^h December 21 at   2^h
January 6 at 1^h January 21 at midnight
February 6 at 23^h February 21 at   22^h
March 6 at 21^h March 21 at   20^h

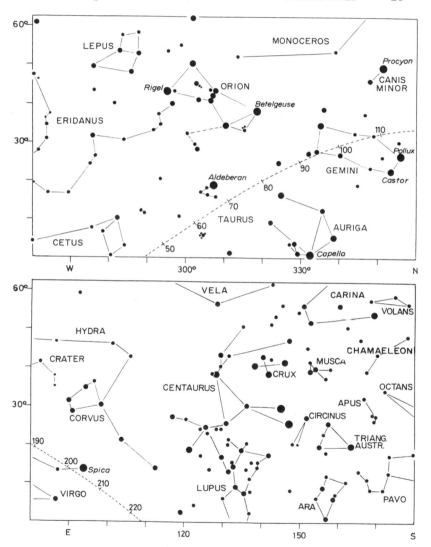

November 6 at	5ʰ	November 21 at	4ʰ
December 6 at	3ʰ	December 21 at	2ʰ
January 6 at	1ʰ	January 21 at	midnight
February 6 at	23ʰ	February 21 at	22ʰ
March 6 at	21ʰ	March 21 at	20ʰ

2R

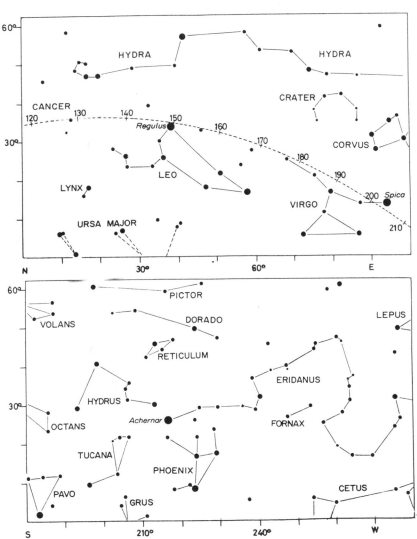

3L

January 6 at 3ʰ	January 21 at 2ʰ
February 6 at 1ʰ	February 21 at midnight
March 6 at 23ʰ	March 21 at 22ʰ
April 6 at 21ʰ	April 21 at 20ʰ
May 6 at 19ʰ	May 21 at 18ʰ

January 6 at 3ʰ   January 21 at   2ʰ
February 6 at 1ʰ   February 21 at midnight
March 6 at 23ʰ   March 21 at   22ʰ
April 6 at 21ʰ   April 21 at   20ʰ
May 6 at 19ʰ   May 21 at   18ʰ

3R

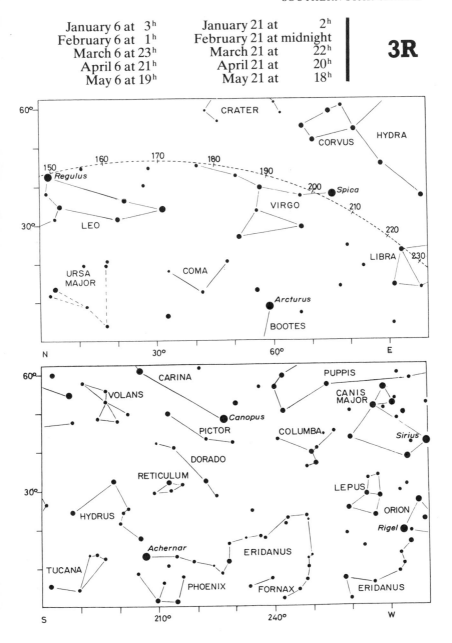

4L

February 6 at 3ʰ	February 21 at 2ʰ
March 6 at 1ʰ	March 21 at midnight
April 6 at 23ʰ	April 21 at 22ʰ
May 6 at 21ʰ	May 21 at 20ʰ
June 6 at 19ʰ	June 21 at 18ʰ

February 6 at 3ʰ   February 21 at   2ʰ
March 6 at 1ʰ   March 21 at midnight
April 6 at 23ʰ   April 21 at   22ʰ
May 6 at 21ʰ   May 21 at   20ʰ
June 6 at 19ʰ   June 21 at   18ʰ

4R

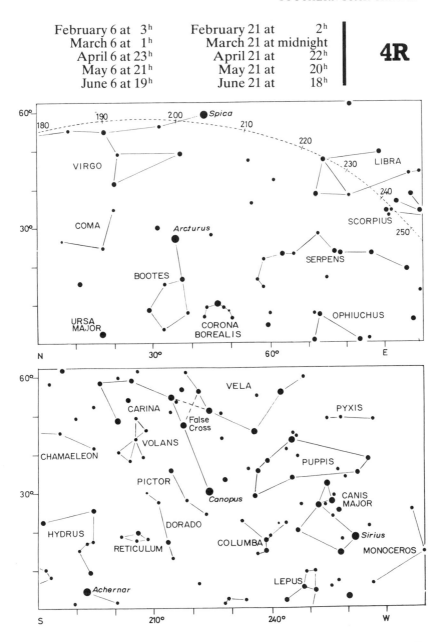

5L

March 6 at 3ʰ	March 21 at 2ʰ
April 6 at 1ʰ	April 21 at midnight
May 6 at 23ʰ	May 21 at 22ʰ
June 6 at 21ʰ	June 21 at 20ʰ
July 6 at 19ʰ	July 21 at 18ʰ

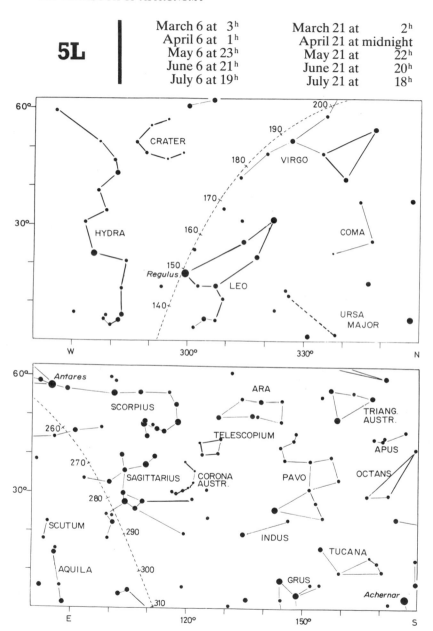

March 6 at 3ʰ   March 21 at 2ʰ
April 6 at 1ʰ   April 21 at midnight
May 6 at 23ʰ   May 21 at 22ʰ
June 6 at 21ʰ   June 21 at 20ʰ
July 6 at 19ʰ   July 21 at 18ʰ

5R

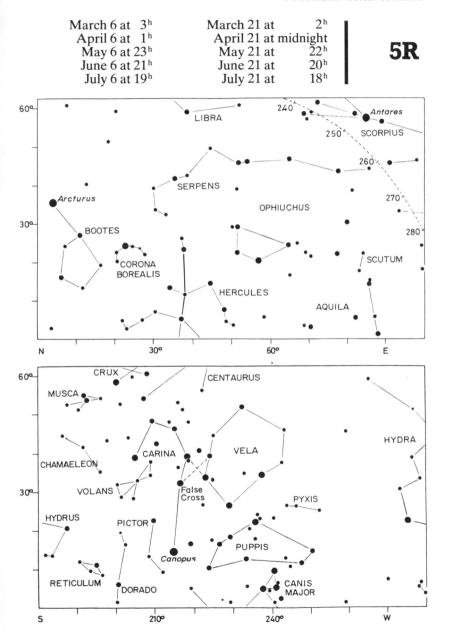

6L

March 6 at 5ʰ
April 6 at 3ʰ
May 6 at 1ʰ
June 6 at 23ʰ
July 6 at 21ʰ

March 21 at 4ʰ
April 21 at 2ʰ
May 21 at midnight
June 21 at 22ʰ
July 21 at 20ʰ

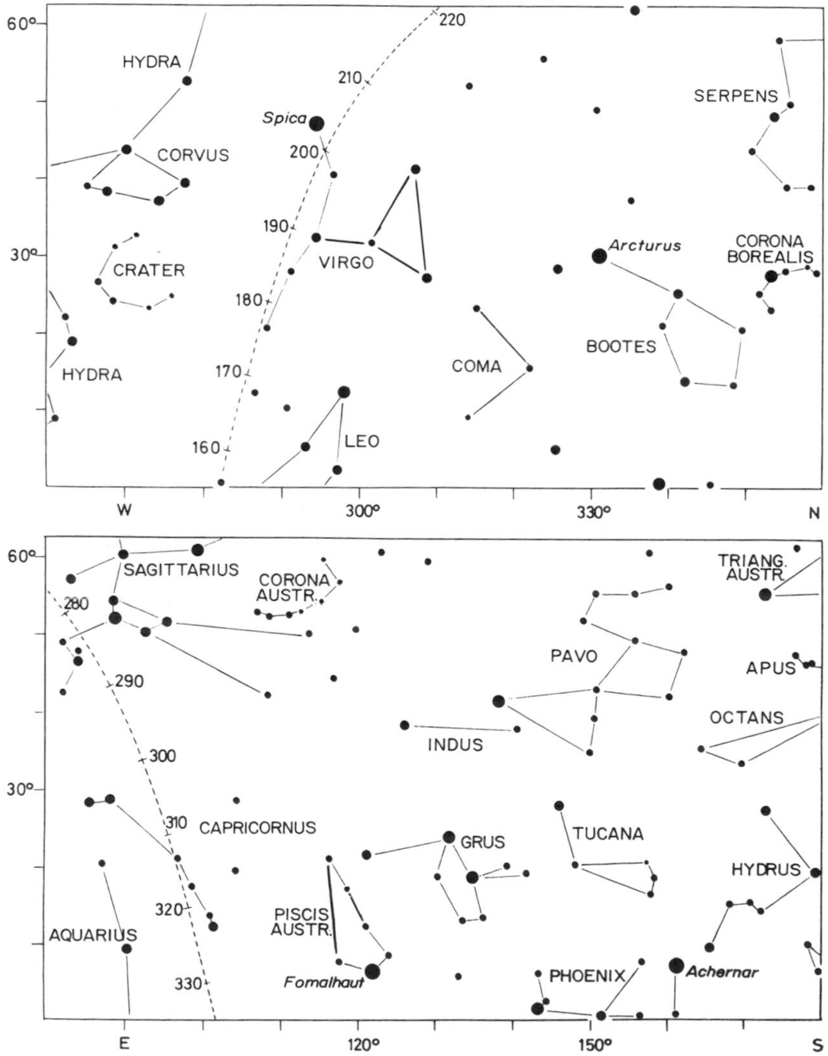

March 6 at 5ʰ   March 21 at   4ʰ
April 6 at 3ʰ   April 21 at   2ʰ
May 6 at 1ʰ   May 21 at midnight
June 6 at 23ʰ   June 21 at   22ʰ
July 6 at 21ʰ   July 21 at   20ʰ

6R

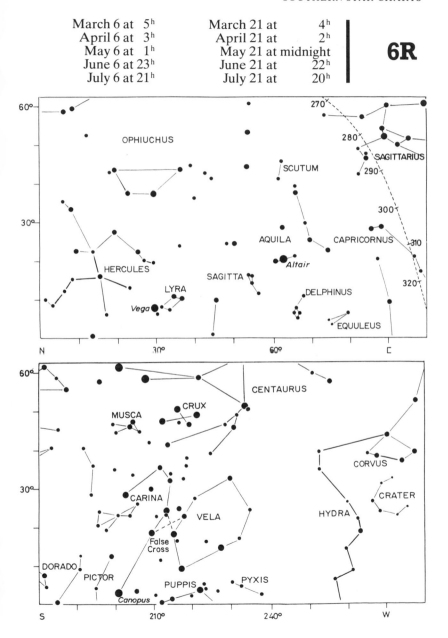

7L

April 6 at 5ʰ	April 21 at 4ʰ
May 6 at 3ʰ	May 21 at 2ʰ
June 6 at 1ʰ	June 21 at midnight
July 6 at 23ʰ	July 21 at 22ʰ
August 6 at 21ʰ	August 21 at 20ʰ

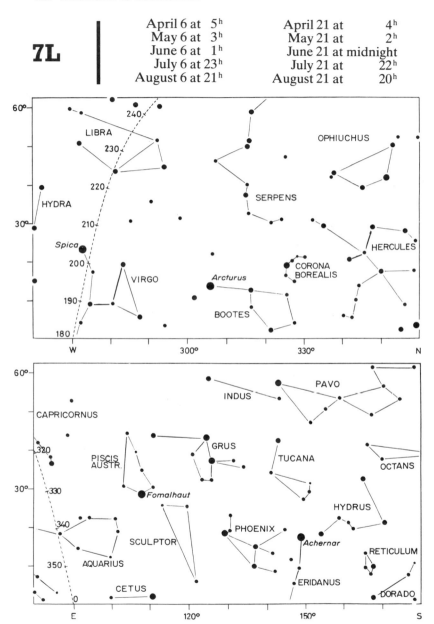

April 6 at 5^h	April 21 at 4^h
May 6 at 3^h	May 21 at 2^h
June 6 at 1^h	June 21 at midnight
July 6 at 23^h	July 21 at 22^h
August 6 at 21^h	August 21 at 20^h

7R

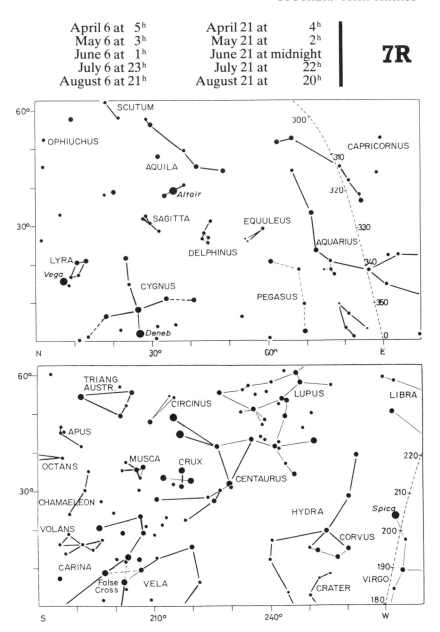

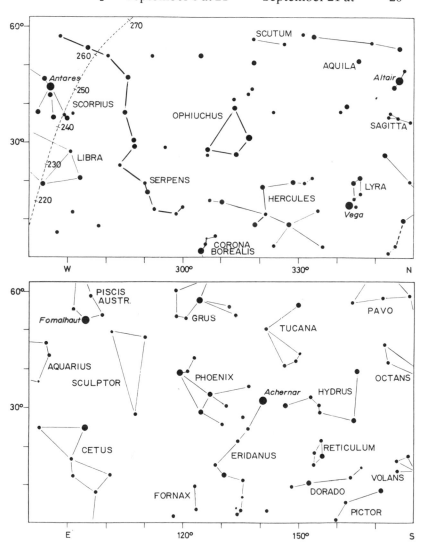

8L

May 6 at   5ʰ   May 21 at   4ʰ
June 6 at   3ʰ   June 21 at   2ʰ
July 6 at   1ʰ   July 21 at midnight
August 6 at 23ʰ   August 21 at   22ʰ
September 6 at 21ʰ   September 21 at   20ʰ

May 6 at 5^h	May 21 at 4^h

May 6 at   5ʰ   May 21 at   4ʰ
June 6 at   3ʰ   June 21 at   2ʰ
July 6 at   1ʰ   July 21 at midnight
August 6 at 23ʰ   August 21 at   22ʰ
September 6 at 21ʰ September 21 at   20ʰ

8R

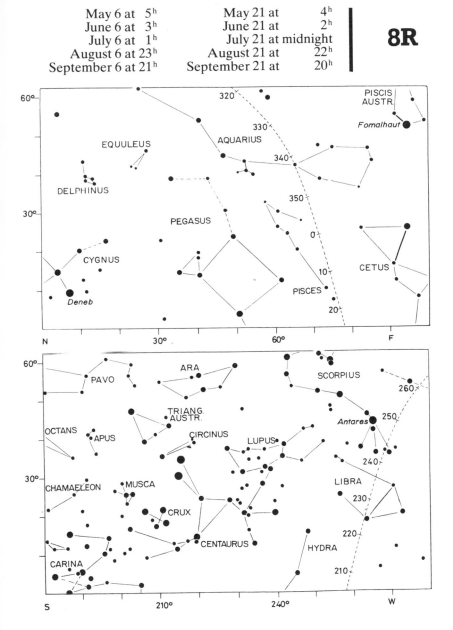

9L

June 6 at 5ʰ   June 21 at 4ʰ
July 6 at 3ʰ   July 21 at 2ʰ
August 6 at 1ʰ   August 21 at midnight
September 6 at 23ʰ   September 21 at 22ʰ
October 6 at 21ʰ   October 21 at 20ʰ

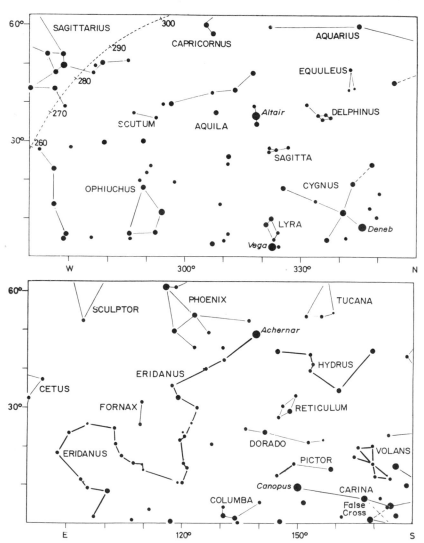

June 6 at 5ʰ   June 21 at 4ʰ
July 6 at 3ʰ   July 21 at 2ʰ
August 6 at 1ʰ   August 21 at midnight
September 6 at 23ʰ   September 21 at 22ʰ
October 6 at 21ʰ   October 21 at 20ʰ

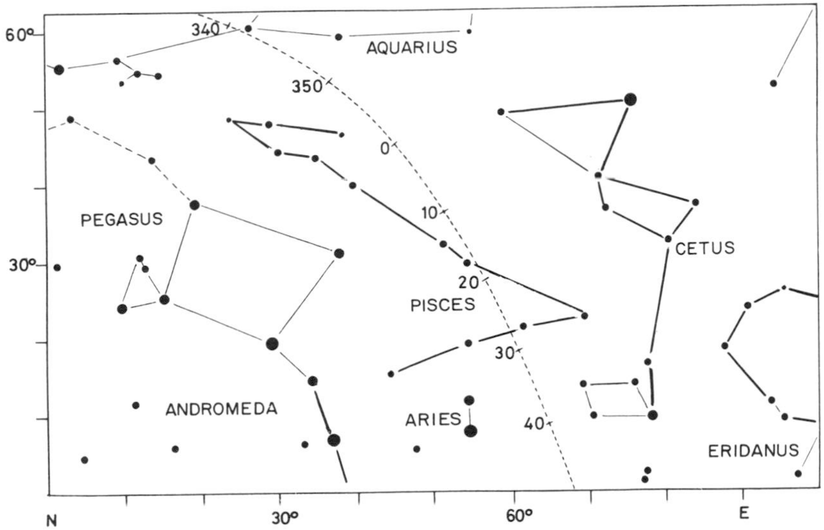

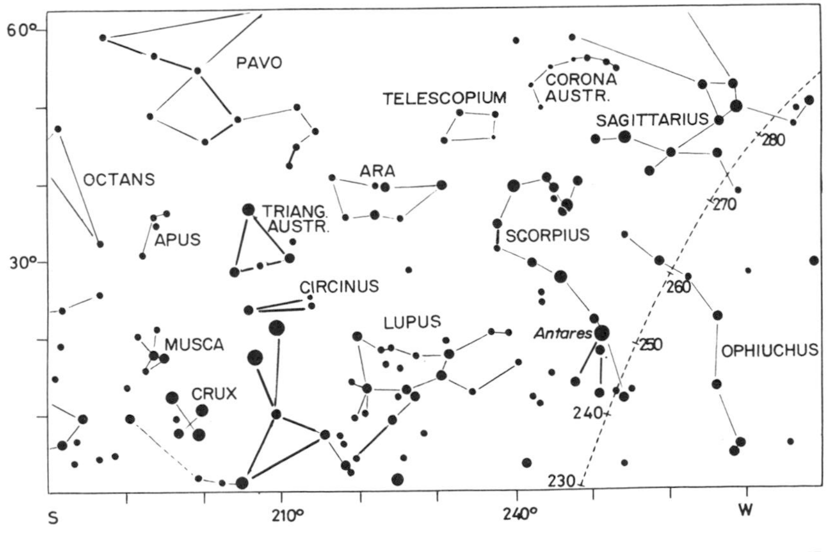

9R

57

10L

July 6 at 5ʰ
August 6 at 3ʰ
September 6 at 1ʰ
October 6 at 23ʰ
November 6 at 21ʰ

July 21 at 4ʰ
August 21 at 2ʰ
September 21 at midnight
October 21 at 22ʰ
November 21 at 20ʰ

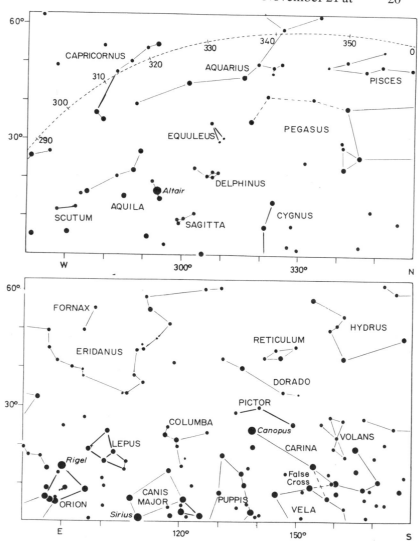

July 6 at   5ʰ   July 21 at   4ʰ
August 6 at   3ʰ   August 21 at   2ʰ
September 6 at   1ʰ   September 21 at midnight
October 6 at 23ʰ   October 21 at   22ʰ
November 6 at 21ʰ   November 21 at   20ʰ

10R

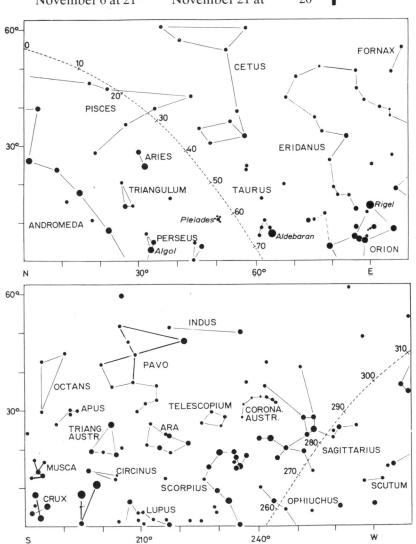

11L

August 6 at   5ʰ   August 21 at   4ʰ
September 6 at   3ʰ   September 21 at   2ʰ
October 6 at   1ʰ   October 21 at midnight
November 6 at 23ʰ   November 21 at   22ʰ
December 6 at 21ʰ   December 21 at   20ʰ

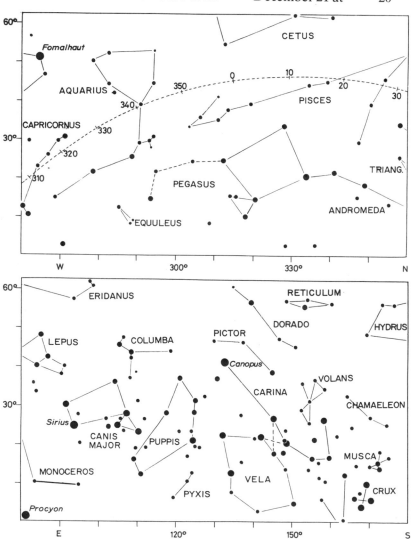

August 6 at 5[h]	August 21 at 4[h]	
September 6 at 3[h]	September 21 at 2[h]	**11R**
October 6 at 1[h]	October 21 at midnight	
November 6 at 23[h]	November 21 at 22[h]	
December 6 at 21[h]	December 21 at 20[h]	

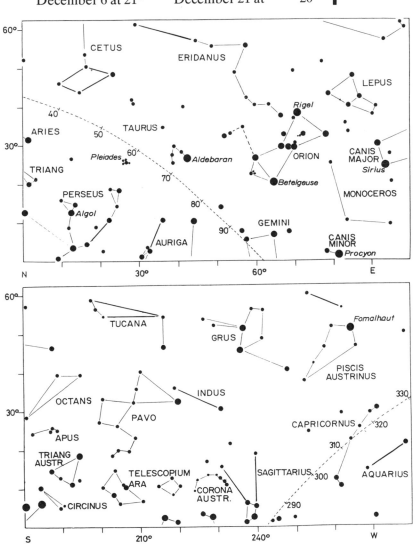

12L

September 6 at 5ʰ   September 21 at 4ʰ
October 6 at 3ʰ   October 21 at 2ʰ
November 6 at 1ʰ   November 21 at midnight
December 6 at 23ʰ   December 21 at 22ʰ
January 6 at 21ʰ   January 21 at 20ʰ

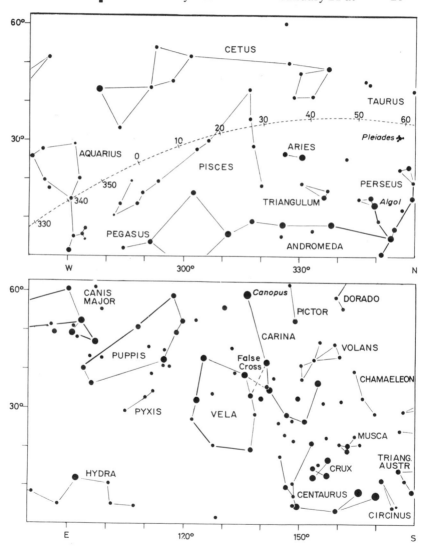

September 6 at 5^h September 21 at   4^h
October 6 at 3^h October 21 at   2^h
November 6 at 1^h November 21 at midnight
December 6 at 23^h December 21 at   22^h
January 6 at 21^h January 21 at   20^h

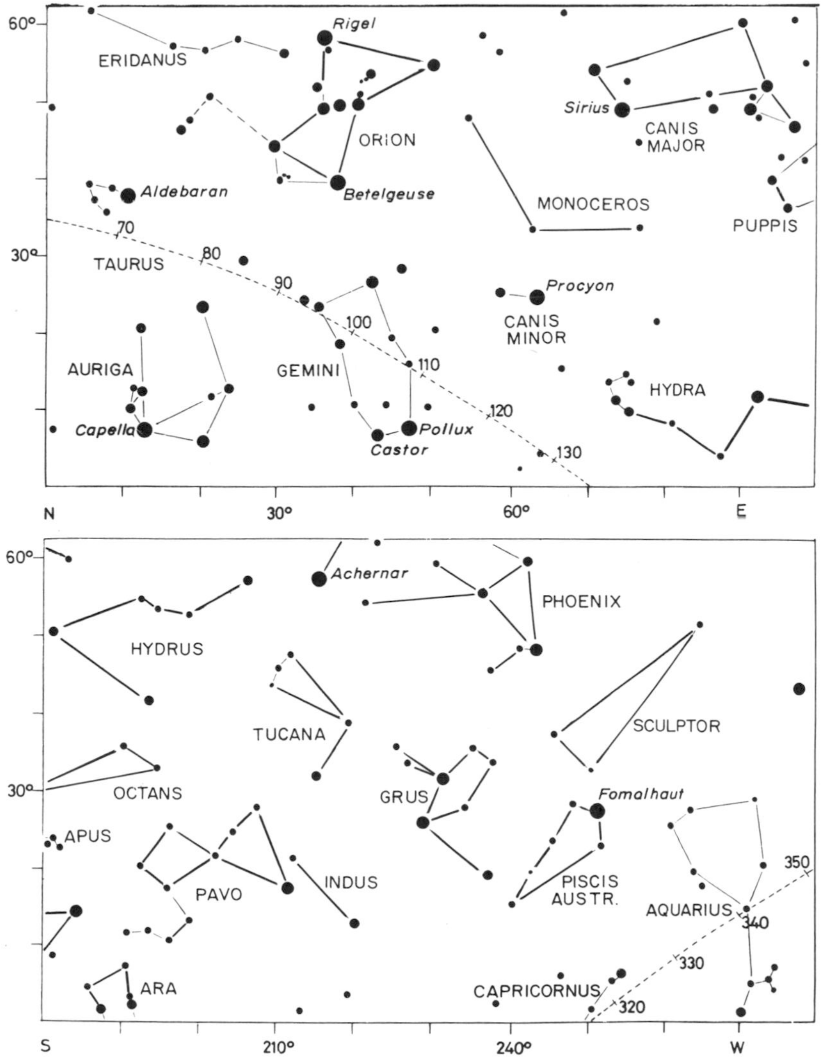

12R

60°

ERIDANUS
Rigel
ORION
Aldebaran
Betelgeuse
MONOCEROS
Sirius
CANIS MAJOR
PUPPIS

70
30°   80
TAURUS   90
100
AURIGA   110
GEMINI   120
Capella   130
Pollux
Castor
Procyon
CANIS MINOR
HYDRA

N   30°   60°   E

60°
Achernar
HYDRUS
PHOENIX
TUCANA
SCULPTOR
OCTANS   GRUS
30°   *Fomalhaut*
APUS
INDUS   PISCIS AUSTR.
PAVO   AQUARIUS   350
340
ARA   330
CAPRICORNUS   320

S   210°   240°   W

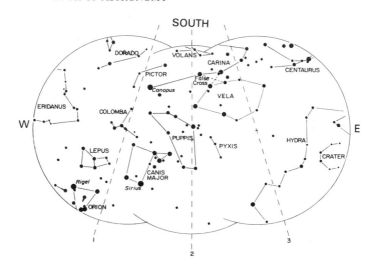

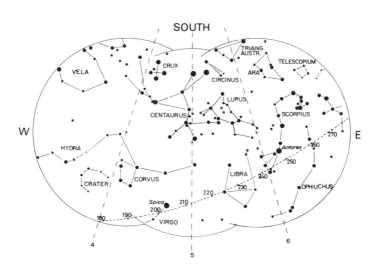

Southern Hemisphere Overhead Stars

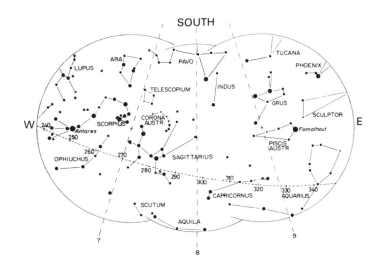

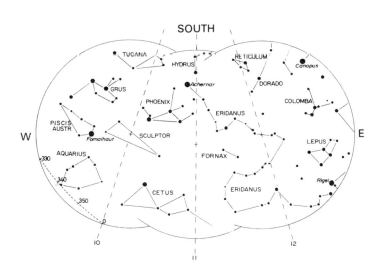

Southern Hemisphere Overhead Stars

The Planets and the Ecliptic

The paths of the planets about the Sun all lie close to the plane of the ecliptic, which is marked for us in the sky by the apparent path of the Sun among the stars, and is shown on the star charts by a broken line. The Moon and planets will always be found close to this line, never departing from it by more than about 7 degrees. Thus the planets are most favourably placed for observation when the ecliptic is well displayed, and this means that it should be as high in the sky as possible. This avoids the difficulty of finding a clear horizon, and also overcomes the problem of atmospheric absorption, which greatly reduces the light of the stars. Thus a star at an altitude of 10 degrees suffers a loss of 60 per cent of its light, which corresponds to a whole magnitude; at an altitude of only 4 degrees, the loss may amount to two magnitudes.

The position of the ecliptic in the sky is therefore of great importance, and since it is tilted at about 23½ degrees to the equator, it is only at certain times of the day or year that it is displayed to the best advantage. It will be realized that the Sun (and therefore the ecliptic) is at its highest in the sky at noon in midsummer, and at its lowest at noon in midwinter. Allowing for the daily motion of the sky, these times lead to the fact that the ecliptic is highest at midnight in winter, at sunset in the spring, at noon in summer and at sunrise in the autumn. Hence these are the best times to see the planets. Thus, if Venus is an evening star, in the western sky after sunset, it will be seen to best advantage if this occurs in the spring, when the ecliptic is high in the sky and slopes down steeply to the north-west. This means that the planet is not only higher in the sky, but will remain for a much longer period above the horizon. For similar reasons, a morning star will be seen at its best on autumn mornings before sunrise, when the ecliptic is high in the east. The outer planets, which can come to opposition (i.e. opposite the Sun), are best seen when opposition occurs in the winter months, when the ecliptic is high in the sky at midnight.

The seasons are reversed in the Southern Hemisphere, spring beginning at the September Equinox, when the Sun crosses the Equator on its way south, summer begins at the December Solstice, when the Sun is highest in the southern sky, and so on. Thus, the time when the ecliptic is highest in the sky, and therefore best placed for observing the planets, may be summarized as follows:

	Midnight	*Sunrise*	*Noon*	*Sunset*
Northern lats.	December	September	June	March
Southern lats.	June	March	December	September

In addition to the daily rotation of the celestial sphere from east to west, the planets have a motion of their own among the stars. The apparent movement is generally *direct,* i.e. to the east, in the direction of increasing longitude, but for a certain period (which depends on the distance of the planet) this apparent motion is reversed. With the outer planets this *retrograde* motion occurs about the time of opposition. Owing to the different inclination of the orbits of these planets, the actual effect is to cause the apparent path to form a loop, or sometimes an S-shaped curve. The same effect is present in the motion of the inferior planets, Mercury and Venus, but it is not so obvious, since it always occurs at the time of inferior conjunction.

The inferior planets, Mercury and Venus, move in smaller orbits than that of the Earth, and so are always seen near the Sun. They are most obvious at the times of greatest angular distance from the Sun (greatest elongation), which may reach 28 degrees for Mercury, or 47 degrees for Venus. They are then seen as evening stars in the western sky after sunset (at eastern elongations) or as morning stars in the eastern sky before sunrise (at western elongations). The succession of phenomena, conjunctions and elongations, always follows the same order, but the intervals between them are not equal. Thus, if either planet is moving round the far side of its orbit its motion will be to the east, in the same direction in which the Sun appears to be moving. It therefore takes much longer for the planet to overtake the Sun – that is, to come to superior conjunction – than it does when moving round to inferior conjunction, between Sun and Earth. The intervals given in the following table are average values; they remain fairly constant in the case of Venus, which travels in an almost circular orbit. In the case of Mercury, however, conditions vary widely because of the great eccentricity and inclination of the planet's orbit.

		Mercury	Venus
Inferior conj.	to Elongation West	22 days	72 days
Elongation West	to Superior conj.	36 days	220 days
Superior conj.	to Elongation East	36 days	220 days
Elongation East	to Inferior conj.	22 days	72 days

The greatest brilliancy of Venus always occurs about 36 days before or after inferior conjunction. This will be about a month *after* greatest eastern elongation (as an evening star), or a month *before* greatest western elongation (as a morning star). No such rule can be given for Mercury, because its distance from the Earth and the Sun can vary over a wide range.

Mercury is not likely to be seen unless a clear horizon is available. It is seldom seen as much as 10 degrees above the horizon in the twilight sky in northern latitudes, but this figure is often exceeded in the Southern Hemisphere. This favourable condition arises because the maximum elongation of 28 degrees can occur only when the planet is at aphelion (farthest from the Sun), and this point lies well south of the Equator. Northern observers must be content with smaller elongations, which may be as little as 18 degrees at perihelion. In general, it may be said that the most favourable times for seeing Mercury as an evening star will be in spring, some days before greatest eastern elongation; in autumn, it may be seen as a morning star some days after greatest western elongation.

Venus is the brightest of the planets and may be seen on occasions in broad daylight. Like Mercury, it is alternately a morning and an evening star, and will be highest in the sky when it is a morning star in autumn, or an evening star in spring. The phenomena of Venus given in the table above can occur only in the months of January, April, June, August and November, and it will be realized that they do not all lead to favourable apparitions of the planet. In fact, Venus is to be seen at its best as an evening star in northern latitudes when eastern elongation occurs in June. The planet is then well north of the Sun in the preceding spring months, and is a brilliant object in the evening sky over a long period. In the Southern Hemisphere a November elongation is best. For similar reasons, Venus gives a prolonged display as a morning star in the months following western elongation in November (in northern latitudes) or in June (in the Southern Hemisphere).

The superior planets, which travel in orbits larger than that of the Earth, differ from Mercury and Venus in that they can be seen opposite the Sun in the sky. The superior planets are morning stars after conjunction with the Sun, rising earlier each day until they come to opposition. They will then be nearest to the Earth (and therefore at their brightest), and will be on the meridian at midnight, due south in northern latitudes, but due north in the Southern Hemisphere. After opposition they are evening stars, setting earlier each evening until they set in the west with the Sun at the next conjunction. The change in brightness about the time of opposition is most noticeable in the case of Mars, whose distance from the Earth can vary considerably and rapidly. The other superior planets are at such great distances that there is very little change in brightness from one opposition to another. The effect of altitude is, however, of some importance, for at a December opposition in northern latitudes the planet will be among the stars of Taurus or Gemini, and can then be at an altitude of more than 60 degrees in southern England. At a summer opposition, when the planet is in Sagittarius, it may only rise to about 15 degrees above the southern horizon, and so makes a less impressive appearance. In the Southern Hemisphere, the reverse conditions apply; a June opposition being the best, with the planet in Sagittarius at an altitude which can reach 78 degrees above the northern horizon.

Mars, whose orbit is appreciably eccentric, comes nearest to the Earth at an opposition at the end of August. It may then be brighter even than Jupiter, but rather low in the sky in Aquarius for northern observers, though very well placed for those in southern latitudes. These favourable oppositions occur every fifteen or seventeen years (1956, 1971, 1988, 2003) but in the Northern Hemisphere the planet is probably better seen at an opposition in the autumn or winter months, when it is higher in the sky. Oppositions of Mars occur at an average interval of 780 days, and during this time the planet makes a complete circuit of the sky.

Jupiter is always a bright planet, and comes to opposition a month later each year, having moved, roughly speaking, from one Zodiacal constellation to the next.

Saturn moves much more slowly than Jupiter, and may remain in the same constellation for several years. The brightness of Saturn depends on the aspect of its rings, as well as on the distance from Earth and Sun. The rings are now inclined towards the Earth and Sun at quite a small angle, and are opening again after being seen edge-on in 1980. The next passage of both the Earth and the Sun through the ring-plane will not occur until 1995.

Uranus, Neptune, and *Pluto* are hardly likely to attract the attention of observers without adequate instruments, but some notes on their present positions in the sky will be found in the April and June Notes.

Phases of the Moon 1986

New Moon				First Quarter				Full Moon				Last Quarter			
	d	h	m		d	h	m		d	h	m		d	h	m
												Jan.	3	19	47
Jan	10	12	22	Jan.	17	22	13	Jan.	26	00	31	Feb	2	04	41
Feb	9	00	55	Feb.	16	19	55	Feb.	24	15	02	Mar.	3	12	17
Mar.	10	14	52	Mar.	18	16	39	Mar.	26	03	02	Apr.	1	19	30
Apr.	9	06	08	Apr.	17	10	35	Apr.	24	12	46	May	1	03	22
May	8	22	10	May	17	01	00	May	23	20	45	May	30	12	55
June	7	14	00	June	15	12	00	June	22	03	42	June	29	00	53
July	7	04	55	July	14	20	10	July	21	10	40	July	28	15	34
Aug.	5	18	36	Aug.	13	02	21	Aug.	19	18	54	Aug.	27	08	38
Sept.	4	07	10	Sept.	11	07	41	Sept.	18	05	34	Sept.	26	03	17
Oct.	3	18	55	Oct.	10	13	28	Oct.	17	19	22	Oct.	25	22	26
Nov.	2	06	02	Nov.	8	21	11	Nov.	16	12	12	Nov.	24	16	50
Dec.	1	16	43	Dec.	8	08	01	Dec.	16	07	04	Dec.	24	09	17
Dec.	31	03	10												

All times are G. M. T.

Reproduced, with permission, from data supplied by
the Science and Engineering Research Council

Longitudes of the Sun, Moon and Planets in 1986

DATE		Sun °	Moon °	Venus °	Mars °	Jupiter °	Saturn °
January	6	286	224	282	224	319	246
	21	301	64	301	233	323	247
February	6	317	277	321	242	327	248
	21	332	108	340	251	330	249
March	6	345	288	356	258	333	250
	21	0	116	15	267	337	250
April	6	16	338	35	274	340	250
	21	31	163	53	281	344	249
May	6	45	13	71	287	346	248
	21	60	200	89	291	349	247
June	6	75	58	109	293	351	246
	21	90	253	126	292	352	245
July	6	104	91	144	289	353	244
	21	118	292	161	285	353	243
August	6	133	136	178	282	352	243
	21	148	344	194	282	351	243
September	6	163	184	209	286	349	244
	21	178	31	221	291	347	245
October	6	193	222	229	299	345	246
	21	207	64	230	307	344	247
November	6	223	275	223	317	343	249
	21	239	108	216	327	343	251
December	6	254	314	217	337	344	253
	21	269	140	226	347	346	254

Longitude of *Uranus* 261°
  Neptune 275°

Moon: Longitude of ascending node
  Jan. 1: 36°   Dec 31: 17°

Mercury moves so quickly among the stars that it is not possible to indicate its position on the star charts at a convenient interval. The monthly notes must be consulted for the best times at which the planet may be seen.

The positions of the other planets are given in the table on the previous page. This gives the apparent longitudes on dates which correspond to those of the star charts, and the position of the planet may at once be found near the ecliptic at the given longitude.

Examples
In the southern hemisphere two planets are seen in the eastern morning sky in February. Identify them.

The southern star charts 4L and 4R shows the eastern sky at February 6^d3^h and shows longitudes $180° - 280°$
Reference to the table opposite gives the the longitude of Mars as 251° and that of Saturn as 249°, on February 21. Thus these planets are found to the north of Antares and the one with the slightly reddish tint is Mars.

The positions of the Sun and Moon can be plotted on the star maps in the same manner as for the planets. The average daily motion of the Sun is 1°, and of the Moon 13°. For the Moon an indication of its position relative to the ecliptic may be obtained from a consideration of its longitude relative to that of the ascending node. The latter changes only slowly during the year as will be seen from the values given on the opposite page. Let us call the difference in longitude of Moon-node, d. Then if d = 0°, 180° or 360° the Moon is on the ecliptic. If d = 90° the Moon is 5° north of the ecliptic and if d = 270° the Moon is 5° south of the ecliptic.

On July 21 the Moon's longitude is given as 292° and the longitude of the node is found by interpolation to be about 25°. Thus d = 267° and the Moon is about 5° south of the ecliptic. Its position may be plotted on northern star charts 7L and 9R: and southern star charts 5L, 6L, 6R, 9L, 10L, 10R and 11R.

Some Events in 1987

In 1987 there will two eclipses, both of the Sun.

March 29: annular-total eclipse of the Sun – southern part of South America, Antarctica, Africa, extreme south-eastern Europe, south-west Asia.

September 23: annular eclipse of the Sun – Asia, Australasia.

THE PLANETS

Mercury may be seen more easily from northern latitudes in the evenings about the time of greatest eastern elongation (February 12) and in the mornings around greatest western elongation (July 25). In the Southern Hemisphere the corresponding dates are March 26 (mornings) and October 4 (evenings).

Venus is visible in the mornings until July and in the evenings from October onwards.

Mars is an evening object for the first half of the year and in the mornings from November onwards.

Jupiter is at opposition on October 18.

Saturn is at opposition on June 9.

Uranus is at opposition on June 16.

Neptune is at opposition on June 28.

Pluto is at opposition on April 29.

January

New Moon: January 10   *Full Moon:* January 26

Earth is at perihelion (nearest to the Sun) on January 2 at a distance of 147 million kilometres.

Mercury is approaching superior conjunction and observers in northern temperate latitudes will not be able to see the planet. Observers in equatorial and southern latitudes will be able to see Mercury as a morning object, magnitude -0.4, low above the east-southeast horizon around the time of beginning of morning civil twilight, for the first ten days of the month.

Venus passes through superior conjunction on January 19 and remains too close to the Sun for observation throughout the month.

Mars magnitude $+1.4$, is visible as a morning object, low in the south-eastern sky for several hours before twilight inhibits observation. Figure 1 shows the path of the planet during January and February as it moves eastwards through Libra and Scorpius into Ophiuchus. The slightly reddish tint of Mars should assist in its identification.

Jupiter magnitude -1.6, is visible as an evening object low in the south-western sky. Jupiter is in Capricornus.

Saturn magnitude $+0.8$, is a morning object in the south-eastern sky. Its path amongst the stars is shown in figure 1.

HALLEY'S COMET. The comet is now approaching perihelion. It has moved south of the celestial equator, and on January 13 it will be close to Jupiter and the crescent Moon, in Aquarius. The average distance from Earth this month is just over 200,000 million

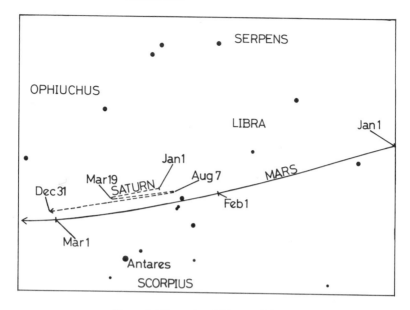

Figure 1. The paths of Mars and Saturn.

kilometres. This will be the last month for naked-eye viewers in the Northern Hemisphere, and by the end of January the comet will be more or less lost in the evening twilight. The position on January 1 is RA 22ʰ 16ᵐ, declination S.2°20′: on January 20, RA 21ʰ 38ᵐ, declination S.6°17′; on January 30, RA 21ʰ 2ᵐ, declination S.8°10′.

In most past returns the comet has developed its tail fully only after perihelion, and this may well be the case in 1986. It is unfortunate that the return is so unfavourable – it is in fact the worst for the past 2000 years, and that of the year 2061 will be no better. It will be a long time before Halley's Comet makes as good a showing as it did in 1910.

THE BELT OF ORION. During evenings in January, Orion dominates the scene; it is crossed by the celestial equator, which passes very close to Mintaka (Delta Orionis) in the Hunter's Belt, so that the constellation is visible from every inhabited continent. Its two leading stars, the orange-red Betelgeux and the brilliant white Rigel, cannot be mistaken. Rigel is 60,000 times as luminous as the

Sun; it is interesting to note that Saiph or Kappa Orionis, one of the stars making up the main pattern, is almost as powerful, though it is much further away.

The three stars of the Belt are:

Star	Magnitude	Luminosity Sun = 1	Distance, light-years
Delta (Mintaka)	2.23v	25,000	2350
Epsilon (Alnilam)	1.70	26,000	1200
Zeta (Alnitak)	1.77	19,000	1100

All are very hot and bluish-white; Mintaka and Alnitak are of spectral type 9.5, while Alnilam is B0. Since all are very remote, their distances are naturally somewhat uncertain, but the values given above are of the right order.

Mintaka is an eclipsing binary with a small range of less than 0.2 magnitude, and a period of 5.7 days. The components are probably about equal in luminosity. There is also a 6.7− magnitude companion at a separation of 52'.8. Probably the two form a physical pair, with a separation of almost half a light-year. Mintaka was the first star known to show stationary spectral lines, due to interstellar matter; the discovery was made by Hartmann, at Potsdam Observatory, in 1904. In 1834 Sir John Herschel announced that Mintaka is variable, with a range of from magnitude 2¼ to 2¾; subsequently Auwers gave a period of 16 days, while Schönfeld could find no regular period. Since the magnitude range is in fact too small to be noticed with the naked eye, these estimates were certainly erroneous.

Alnilam is surrounded by the faint nebula NGC 1990. Alnitak is a triple system. In 1819 Kunowsky discovered the double nature of the main star; the magnitudes are 1.9 and 5.5, and the separation is 2'.6. The real separation is aboubt 1300 astronomical units, and the revolution period must be very long. A third component, of magnitude 10, lies at a distance of 57'.6, and is probably not genuinely associated with the main pair. The famous Horse's Head dark nebula lies south of Alnitak; it is spectacular when photographed, but remarkably difficult to observe visually.

The difference in magnitude between Alnilam and Alnitak is only 0.7, but it is quite easy to see that Alnilam is the brighter of the two – a comment upon the sensitivity of the human eye.

*Minimum distance Comet-Moon is at least 12°.

February

New Moon: February 9   *Full Moon:* February 24

Mercury is at superior conjunction on the first day of the month. By the middle of February observers in the Southern Hemisphere will be able to see the planet in the evenings, while those in northern temperate latitudes will have to wait a further week; however, for them this will be the most favourable evening apparition of the year. Figure 2 shows, for observers in latitude N 52°, the changes in azimuth (true bearing from the north through east, south and west) and altitude of Mercury on successive evenings when the Sun is 6° below the horizon. This condition is known as the end of evening civil twilight, and in this latitude and at this time of year occurs about 35 minutes after sunset. The changes in brightness of the planet are roughly indicated by the sizes of the circles marking positions at 5-day intervals, and it will be noticed that Mercury is brightest before it reaches greatest eastern elongation on February 28: its magnitude on February 19 is –1.1, while ten days later it is –0.3.

Venus remains too close to the Sun for observation for most of the month, but at the end begins to be visible in the evenings, for a very short while after sunset. Venus is about 3 magnitudes brighter than Mercury and is closer to the Sun. For observers in the Southern Hemisphere Venus is still too close to the Sun for observation.

Mars is a morning object, magnitude +1.1. Its path amongst the stars is shown in Figure 1 given with the notes for January. Note its proximity to Saturn around the middle of the month.

Jupiter is coming to the end of its evening apparition as it passes through conjunction on February 18. At the beginning of the month it may only be glimpsed with difficulty, low above the south-western horizon at the end of the evening civil twilight.

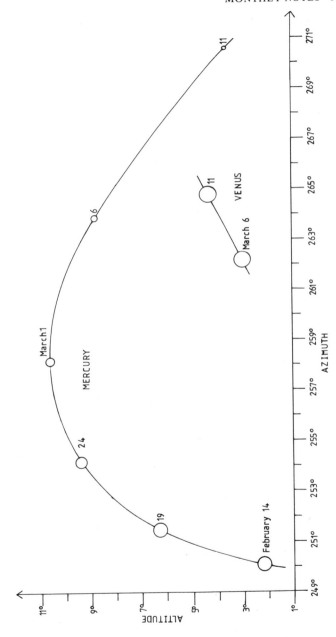

Figure 2. Evening apparition of Mercury for latitude N.52°.

Saturn magnitude +0.7, continues to be visible as a morning object in the south-eastern sky.

HALLEY'S COMET. Perihelion occurs on February 9. The comet is then in Capricornus, but is on the far side of the Sun, and will be invisible from Earth; our only hope of recording it will be from the Pioneer probe now in orbit round the planet Venus. By February 20 the comet will have emerged into the south-eastern sky before dawn, and will be well into the Southern Hemisphere: RA 20^h 43^m, declination S.13°08'. The magnitude may rise to about 3, though, of course, it is always dangerous to make predictions; there may be a considerable tail. This period will mark the start of the best opportunities for studying the comet visually, though only from southern latitudes. Photography will certainly be carried out; see the article by R. Arbour in the *1985 Yearbook*.

ETA CARINÆ. The constellation of Carina, the Keel of the old Ship Argo, is now high in the sky to Southern-Hemisphere observers, though it never rises from the latitude of Britain or New York. Its leading star, Canopus, is second in brilliancy only to Sirius, and Canopus is in fact much the more powerful of the two. However, little more than 140 years ago even Canopus was surpassed by the extraordinary variable Eta Carinæ, which is associated with magnificent nebulosity.

Eta Carinæ is the most erratic star in the sky. It has been known to reach magnitude −1, as it did during the 1830s; but for a long time now it has been just below naked-eye visibility. At its peak it was about 6,000,000 times as luminous as the Sun, far outmatching even Canopus, and was probably the most luminous star in the Galaxy. In fact it is still exceptionally luminous, and its relative dimness in the sky is due in part, at least, to intervening nebulosity; it is very strong at infrared wavelengths.

The nature of Eta Carinæ remains uncertain. There have been suggestions that it may be approaching the climax of its main career, and will explode as a supernova. If it does, it will be truly superb; but we cannot tell when this will happen, if at all. Meanwhile it is always worth using a telesope to look at Eta Carinæ, which is unlike any other object known to us.

THOMAS WRIGHT. Thomas Wright of Durham died two hundred years ago, on February 25, 1786. He was born in 1711, and was apprenticed to a clockmaker at the age of thirteen; he was a natural mathematician, and in 1742 he was even offered the Chair of Mathematics at the St Peterburg Academy of Sciences, though he declined it, and spent the rest of his life in Durham as a writer and teacher. His most famous book was *An Original Theory or New Hypothesis or the Universe,* in which he described the Milky Way as a flattened system, and suggested that the starry nebulæ might be external galaxies. It must, however, be admitted that his main aims were religious, and his attempts to reconcile religion with science sound strange today. Yet he made real advances; and it is worth noting that he supported the theory that Saturn's rings are made up of particles orbiting the planet rather than solid or liquid sheets, though he was not the first to suggest this.

ALPHARD. For northern observers this is a good time to look at Alphard for Alpha Hydræ, nicknamed the 'Solitary One' because of its isolated position; it is rather low in the south, and in line with the Twins, Castor and Pollux. Alphard is decidedly reddish. Its magnitude is almost exactly 2; Sir John Herschel and others have suspected it of variability, though there seems to be no recent evidence that it is anything but constant. It is 115 times as luminous as the Sun, and is 85 light-years away.

March

New Moon: March 10   *Full Moon:* March 26

Summer Time in Great Britain and Northern Ireland may commence on March 23.

Equinox: March 20

Mercury continues to be visible as an evening object for the first ten days of the month, low above the western horizon about half an hour after sunset, Observers in northern temperate latitudes should refer to Figure 2, given with the notes for February. Note the proximity to Venus between March 6 and 11. Mercury passes through inferior conjunction on March 16. During the last week of the month observers in equatorial and southern latitudes will be able to see it as a morning object, low above the eastern horizon at the beginning of morning civil twilight. Mercury has increased in brightness to magnitude +1.3 by the end of the month.

Venus, magnitude –3.4, is visible in the evenings, low above the western horizon for a short while after sunset. However, Venus is moving northwards and observers in the Southern Hemisphere will have difficulty in detecting the planet.

Mars continues to be visible as a morning object, and by the end of the month its magnitude has brightened to +0.3.

Jupiter is unsuitably placed for observation to those in northern temperate latitudes. For observers further south it becomes visible as a morning object during the second half of the month, magnitude –2.0, low in the east before dawn.

Saturn is a morning object on the border of Scorpius and Ophiuchus, north of Antares.

HALLEY'S COMET. This month marks the climax of the current studies of Halley's Comet. No less than five probes will, it is hoped, rendezvous with it. The Russian space-craft Vega 1 will by-pass the comet on March 6; the two Japanese probes, Planet A and MS–T5, on March 8, and Vega 2 on March 9. Then, on the night of March 13–14, the European Space Agency probe Giotto will penetrate the coma, with the aim of sending back direct information from the nucleus.

This is an excellent example of international co-operation. Up to now, nobody has known quite where the nucleus is, because it is hidden inside the coma; we do not even know how big it is, though the diameter can hardly be more than a few kilometres, or a few tens of kilometres at most. The Russian and Japanese space-craft will attempt to find out, and relay the information so that Giotto's trajectory can be corrected at the last moment. The Giotto data will be received by the great radio telescope at Parkes in New South Wales, and the pictures will be electronically assembled at Darmstädt in Germany.

It is essential to transmit the data at once, because there can be little hope that Giotto will survive the encounter. The neighbourhood of the comet is bound to be very hazardous, and it seems inevitable that Giotto will be destroyed by collision with a solid particle, either rocky or icy. The relative speed is extremely high, because the comet has retrograde motion, and the vital part of the encounter will take only a few minutes.

The comet is still moving south. The positions for March are:

	RA		declination S.
	h	m	
March 1	20	27	16°19'
March 20	19	37	26°45'
March 31	18	33	37°25'

By the end of the month the comet will be close to Epsilon Sagittarii, and will be unobservable from Britain, though it will still be accessible from placed north of the equator – anywhere south of approximately latitude 50 degrees north, though obviously it will be seen to better advantage from the Southern Hemisphere. The distance from Earth is still decreasing, though perihelion has passed, and the comet has begun its journey back to the far reaches of the Solar System, travelling tail-first. The magnitude of the nucleus may exceed 3, and the tail is expected to reach its maximum development of up to around 30 degrees. It is unfortunate that the Moon will interfere with observations during the latter part of the month, but in any case the very best chances will occur in April, when for the first week or two the Moon will be unobtrusive.

It is worth remembering that perhaps the most famous of all returns of Halley's Comet was a March one: in 1066, when Duke William of Normandy was preparing to invade England. Perihelion took place late in the month. Rather curiously, there are no reports of sightings until after perihelion, but the comet was followed from April through June, and was apparently bright. Zonares, the Greek historian, commented that it 'was as large as the Moon'.

There is no reason to doubt the story that the comet was regarded as an unfavourable omen by the Saxon court of King Harold. The scene is shown on the famous Bayeux Tapestry, which is said by some authorities to have been embroidered by the Conqueror's wife, though others believe that it was commissioned either by her or by the somewhat fierce Bishop Odo of Bayeux. By the time of the Battle of Hastings the comet had faded from the sky, but the memory of it remained.

April

New Moon: April 9   *Full Moon:* April 24

Mercury, for observers in northern temperate latitudes, is too close to the Sun for observation throughout April, but for observers further south this is their best morning apparition of the year; Mercury reaches greatest western elongation (28°) on April 13. Figure 3 shows the changes in azimuth and altitude of Mercury on successive mornings for observers in latitude S.35°, when the Sun is 6° below the horizon – a condition known as the beginning of morning civil twilight, which in this latitude at this time of year is about 30 minutes before sunrise. Mercury's brightness increases

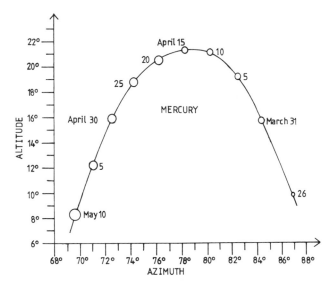

Figure 3. Morning apparition of Mercury for latitude S.35°.

slowly during the month, its magnitude being +1.2 at the beginning and −0.3 at the end.

Venus continues to be visible for a while in the evenings, low in the western sky after sunset. It has a magnitude of −3.3.

Mars is continuing to brighten as it moves closer to the Earth (reaching opposition in July) and is visible as a morning object in Sagittarius. Its path amongst the stars is shown in Figure 5, given with the notes for June.

Jupiter, magnitude −1.6, is a morning object visible above the eastern horizon before dawn though observers in northern temperate latitudes are unlikely to detect it until the last week of the month. Jupiter is in Aquarius and remains in that constellation for the rest of the year.

Saturn, magnitude +0.4, continues to be visible in the morning sky.

HALLEY'S COMET. With the excitement of the space-craft missions over, we now come to the very best period for observing Halley's Comet from Earth, though only from the Southern Hemisphere. The track against the stars is shown in Figure 4. On April 10 the RA is $15^h 22^m$ and the declination S.47° 23′, completely out of view from European latitudes. During the month the motion will carry the comet from Corona Australis through Scorpius, Ara, Norma, Lupus, Centaurus and finally into Hydra, which it will reach by April 30 and therefore accessible once more from British latitudes. Before dawn in mid-April it will be almost overhead from places such as South Africa and Australia, and the magnitude of the coma may be anything between 2 and 3½, with a tail which is expected to reach at least 30 degrees. Closest approach to the Earth occurs on April 11, and after that date the fading will be rapid; by the time it reaches Hydra the magnitude may have dropped below naked-eye visibility, though the comet will still be a very easy binocular object.

The Moon will cause interference later in the month, but there will be an exceptionally rare spectacle on the 24th, because a total lunar eclipse will occur. The light of the Moon will be dimmed, and the comet will show up to advantage – an opportunity for astronomical photographers.

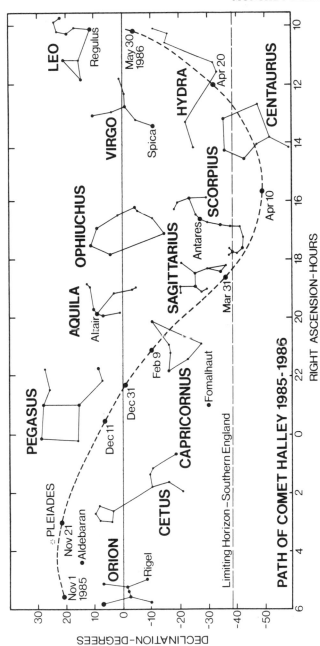

Figure 4. Track of Halley's Comet against the stars.

It is hoped that amateur observers will be very much on the alert during the whole of this month. There can be very rapid changes in the form and structure of the tail, and it is important to keep watch as continuously as possible. There is official amateur participation in the International Halley Watch, and there is always the chance that an amateur photograph may be of great value. No doubt Halley's Comet will be the most-photographed comet in all history!

THE SOLAR ECLIPSE. In addition to the lunar eclipse of April 24, when totality will last for 1 hour and 8 minutes, there will be a solar eclipse on April 9. However, this will be well seen only from the Antarctic. It will not be total anywhere; the maximum obscuration is 82 per cent – so that there will be no chance of seeing the chromosphere, the corona, or the prominences with the naked eye.

May

Mercury continues to be visible as a morning object for the first two weeks of the month, though not for observers in northern temperate latitudes. Other observers should refer to Figure 3 in the notes for April. During this period of visibility the magnitude of the planet brightens from −0.3 to −1.3. Mercury passes through superior conjunction on May 23.

Venus continues to be visible as an evening object, low in the western sky after sunset. Venus attains its maximum northerly declination towards the end of the month, and for observers in southern Britain it sets about two hours after the Sun.

Mars continues to be visible as a bright object in the sky after midnight, its magnitude increasing from −0.4 to −1.3 during the month.

Jupiter, magnitude −1.8, is a morning object, visible in the south-eastern sky before dawn. The path of Jupiter among the stars is shown in Figure 8 which is given with the notes for December.

Saturn, magnitude +0.2, reaches opposition on May 28 and therefore is available for observation throughout the night. The rings of Saturn, which are a beautiful sight even in small telescopes, are well open.

HALLEY'S COMET. The best of the return is now past and the comet is receding from both the Sun and the Earth. On May 1 the position is RA 10ʰ 59ᵐ, declination S.19°14', very close to the star Alkes or Alpha Crateris. Whether the comet will still be visible with the naked eye remains to be seen; very probably it will not, and there is little doubt that naked-eye observers will lose it well before the end of the month. This does not mean that amateur observers will have come to the end of their programme. Every effort should be made to continue monitoring the comet so long as it stays within range.

It may be of interest to list the returns of Halley's Comet since records began. According to Dr Joseph Brady, the comet reported in B.C. 2647 was probably Halley's, but we really begin in B.C. 1059. Most of the early observations are Chinese. It will be seen that the period is not always 76 years; there are marked variations, due to the perturbations of the planets upon the comet. So here is the list:

Year	Date of Perihelion	Remarks
B.C. 1059	Dec. 3	Recorded
240	May 25	Definitely seen in China
164	Nov. 12	Observed by Babylonians
87	Aug. 6	Observed
12	Oct. 10	Observed August/October
A.D. 66	Jan. 25	Observed Jan./Apr. Bright
141	Mar. 22	Fairly close approach (0.17 a.u.)
218	May 17	Observed Apr./May
295	Apr. 20	Seen during May only
374	Feb. 16	Approach within 0.09 a.u. Bright
451	Jun. 28	Observed Jne./Aug.
530	Sept. 27	Observed Aug./Sept.
607	Mar. 15	Some uncertainty; one of two comets of this year was Halley's
684	Oct. 2	Drawn for the first time; sketch published in the Nürnberg Chronicle in 1493
760	May 20	Brilliant, 'like a great beam'
837	Feb. 28	Most favourable of all returns; brighter than Venus, with a 93° tail. The comet came within 6,000,000 km of the Earth
912	July 18	Much less brilliant; seen only in July

989	Sept. 5	Observed Aug./Sept. but not well documented
1066	Mar. 20	Very bright; recorded in Bayeux Tapestry
1145	Apr. 18	Observed Apr./July. Well documented
1222	Sept. 28	Observed Sept./Oct. Not a brilliant return
1301	Oct. 25	Very bright. Seen by the painter Giotto di Bondone, who used it as the Star of Bethlehem in his picture *The Adoration of the Magi*
1378	Nov. 10	Observed Sept./Nov, but not a good return
1456	June 9	Bright. Pope Calixtus III preached against it as an agent of the Devil!
1531	Aug. 26	Followed by Peter Apian. Not a brilliant return, but quite conspicuous
1607	Oct. 27	Observed by Kepler; a good return. The head was of around magnitude $-2\frac{1}{2}$
1682	Sept. 15	Observed by Edmond Halley
1759	Mar. 13	First predicted return; followed Dec.1758/June 1759
1835	Nov. 16	Good return; minimum distance form Earth 0.05 a.u.
1910	Apr. 20	Good return; first photographs
1986	Feb. 9	Present return

THE MAGNITUDE OF SATURN. When it reaches opposition this month, Saturn, at magnitude 0.2, is brighter than any star in the sky apart from Sirius, Canopus, Alpha Centauri, Arcturus, Vega, Capella, and Rigel. This is because the rings are wide open – and the rings have a higher albedo than the planet itself; when the rings are edgewise-on, as they were in 1980 and will be again in 1995, the opposition magnitude is only about the same as that of Aldebaran.

The intervals between successive edgewise presentations are 13 years 9 months and 15 years and 9 months. During the shorter interval the south pole is tilted towards the Sun, the southern ring-face is seen, and the planet passes through perihelion. At the moment it is the northern hemisphere which is tilted sunwards, so that part of Saturn's southern hemisphere is covered by the rings.

June

New Moon: June 7   *Full Moon:* June 22

Solstice: June 21

Mercury attains greatest eastern elongation on June 25 (25°) and will be visible as an evening object throughout the month. Because of the long duration of twilight, observers in northern temperate latitudes will have difficulty in locating the planet; under good conditions they may be able to detect it low above the west-north-west horizon at about the time of the end of evening civil twilight, but only around the middle of the month.

Venus, now over 30° from the Sun, is a brilliant object in the western sky in the evenings, magnitude −3.4. Observers in northern temperate latitudes will find that, relative to the time of sunset Venus is setting earlier even though its angular distance from the Sun continues to increase: this is because Venus is now moving southwards in declination.

Mars, its magnitude brightening from −1.3 to −2.2, continues to be a brilliant object in the morning sky and becomes visible well before midnight. Mars is moving slowly in Sagittarius, and its path amongst the stars for the period around opposition is shown in Figure 5. It reaches its first stationary point on June 10.

Jupiter, magnitude −2.0, continues to be visible as a morning object in the south-eastern sky.

Saturn, remains a prominent object in the night sky, magnitude +0.3. Its path amongst the stars is shown in Figure 1 given with the notes for January.

HALLEY'S COMET. The movement of the comet has slowed down; it remains in Sextans, but it has now fallen in magnitude so much that telescopes of some size will be needed to show it. We must reconcile ourselves to the fact that the best of the 1986 return is well and truly over.

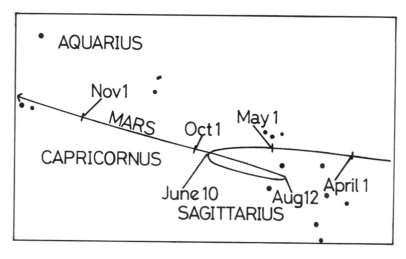

Figure 5. The path of Mars.

THE NEIGHBOURS OF ANTARES. The constellation of Scorpius or Scorpio, the Scorpion, is one of the most magnificent in the sky. It is well south of the celestial equator, and is always rather low down from British latitudes; the 'sting', which contains one star (Shaula) only just below the first magnitude, barely rises even from southern England, and part of the constellation remains permanently below the horizon, though all of it can be fairly well seen from most of the United States. This is the best time of the year for seeing it. From countries such as South Africa, Australia and New Zealand, the Scorpion is almost overhead during evenings, and dominates the night sky. (The names are optional. Scorpius is the more correct, and is preferred by astronomers; astrologers usually refer to Scorpio.)

The brightest star in the constellation is the red supergiant Antares, with a magnitude of 0.96 (very slightly variable); it is the reddest of all the brilliant stars, though it is rivalled by Betelgeux in Orion. Antares is 7500 times as luminous as the Sun, and 330 light-years away. It has a greenish companion of magnitude 6.5, at a delicate details, and it must be admitted that to the owner of a small telescope (say a 76mm refractor) Mars is a much less rewarding object than Jupiter or Saturn. Moreover, it can be well seen for only a month or two to either side of opposition. During 1986 things are made worse, from the viewpoint of the Northern-Hemisphere observer, by the fact that Mars is in Sagittarius – about as far south as it can ever move, though, of course, this means that southern observers can see the planet almost overhead.

The two midget satellites, Phobos and Deimos, are not easy objects, and the best way to see them is to mask the image of Mars itself by an occulting disk; however, even this will not allow the satellites to be seen with any telescope of much under 30cm aperture. They are quite unlike our massive Moon, since they are irregular in shape; Phobos has a longest diameter of a mere 28 kilometres, while Deimos is even smaller. It is quite likely that both are ex-asteroids which were captured by Mars in the distant past, though admittedly this involves some special circumstances, and the theory has definite weaknesses.

EGA. The lovely blue star Vega is now almost overhead during venings in British latitudes. From Australia or South Africa it ever rises high above the horizon, though it is obvious enough; bservers in the southernmost part of New Zealand will be lucky to e it at all.

distance of 2″.9; the companion is notable because it is a radio source. It is not too easy to see with small telescopes, because it is so overpowered by the glare of its primary. The green hue is due largely to contrast.

Flanking Antares to either side are two much fainter stars, Sigma Scorpii or Alniyat to the north and Tau Scorpii to the south; Tau has not been given a proper name, though it is actually a little brighter than Sigma.

Sigma, with an apparent magnitude of 2.9, is very slightly variable in light. It belongs to the so-called Beta Cephei or Beta Canis Majoris class; these are pulsating, but the magnitude range is very slight – only about a tenth of a magnitude in the case of Sigma Scorpii, whose period is 5 hours 55 minutes. Sigma has a distant companion of the 9th magnitude, which shares its motion through space; the main star is a spectroscopic binary. The luminosity is 5,000 times that of the Sun, and the distance is thought to be about 580 light-years, considerably greater than that of Antares.

Tau Scorpii, with an apparent magnitude of 2.8, is a single star, 780 light-years away and with roughly the same luminosity as Sigma; like Sigma, it is bluish-white, with a spectrum of Type B. Seen from Earth, both Sigma and Tau seem vastly inferior to Antares, but this is mainly an effect of their greater distance.

Also in this region is the fine globular cluster M.4, which is easily seen in binoculars and is on the fringe of naked-eye visibility. Its distance is believed to be in the region of 6000 light-years, but with considerable uncertainty because of the presence of major obscuring interstellar clouds near it. It is certainly one of the closest of the globular clusters – much nearer than, for example, Omega Centauri, 47 Tucanæ or M.13 Herculis – and it is easy to find, because it lies only slightly away from a line joining Antares to Sigma, and is in the same binocular field with them. It was discovered by De Chéseaux in 1746, and is rather less condensed than most globulars. Even when low down, as it always is from Britain, it is well worth finding, and from southern latitudes it is one of the most impressive globular clusters in the sky.

July

New Moon: July 7   *Full Moon:* July 21

Earth is at aphelion (farthest from the Sun) on July 5 at a distance of 152 million kilometres.

Mercury remains invisible to observers in northern temperate latitudes, but for those further south it will continue to be observable low in the western sky at the end of evening civil twilight for the first half of the month. Mercury passes through inferior conjunction on July 23.

Venus continues to be visible as an evening object, magnitude −3.6, above the western horizon after sunset. Venus passes north of Regulus on July 10, at the same time as the crescent Moon passes north of the planet.

Mars reaches opposition on July 10, magnitude −2.4, and is then the brightest object in the night sky apart from Venus and the Moon. The orbit of Mars is so eccentric that its closest approach to the Earth (61 million kilometres) does not occur until six days after opposition.

Jupiter is visible in the south-eastern sky in the mornings, and now well above the horizon before midnight. It has a magnitude of −2.2.

Saturn, magnitude +0.5, continues to be visible in the south-western sky in the evenings.

HALLEY'S COMET. Amateurs are having their last view of the comet. It is still in Sextans, but has faded so much that it is becoming difficult to see in binoculars, and in addition it is becoming inconveniently close to the Sun in the sky. Make the most of your

final opportunities! The distance from Earth is now 40(kilometres, and is increasing steadily; the comet has move beyond the orbit of Mars, though it is still closer-in tha

MARS AT OPPOSITION. This year finds Mars at one of oppositions, since the planet is not far from perihelion; much more eccentric than that of the Earth, which oppositions are so unequal. The minimum distance is kilometres, at the aphelic opposition of 1980 the planet v close as 101,000,000 kilometres. This year is one of the r when Mars can rival Jupiter in brilliance; in fact it is now brighter of the two, and is surpassed only by Venus. T diameter reaches 23.1 seconds of arc. At the 1988 op maximum apparent diameter will be slightly greater, at of arc, but all oppositions for the rest of the century will favourable, and in 1995 the magnitude will not excee Mars will remain considerably fainter than Sirius.

Even small telescopes will show surface features month, provided that seeing conditions are reasonat main dark areas are to all intents and purposes perm: they show slight variations in extent and colour; the V Major, in the southern hemisphere, was clearly drawr Huygens as long ago as 1659, and the polar caps were by G. D. Cassini in 1666. It was long claimed that v caps shrink, in the Martian spring and early summer become more definite, as though they were due to o revived by moisture wafted from the caps by the Ma is is now known that the dark regions are not orgar are they old sea-beds (the Syrtis Major is a lofty so-called 'wave of darkening' seems to have been an as were the celebrated canals drawn so firmly by and many others.

Mars rotates on its axis in a period of $24^h 37^m 22^s.6$ day, or 'sol', is more than half an hour longer than (is observed on successive nights, it is easy to see t are displaced, and the shifts can be noticed over few minutes, though they are less pronounced tha larger and quicker-spinning Jupiter.

When observing Mars, it is desirable to magnification as is possible without losing shar image. This means that telescopes of fair size a

final opportunities! The distance from Earth is now 400,000,000 kilometres, and is increasing steadily; the comet has moved out well beyond the orbit of Mars, though it is still closer-in than Jupiter.

MARS AT OPPOSITION. This year finds Mars at one of its closer oppositions, since the planet is not far from perihelion; its orbit is much more eccentric than that of the Earth, which is why the oppositions are so unequal. The minimum distance is 61,000,000 kilometres, at the aphelic opposition of 1980 the planet was never as close as 101,000,000 kilometres. This year is one of the rare periods when Mars can rival Jupiter in brilliance; in fact it is now slightly the brighter of the two, and is surpassed only by Venus. The apparent diameter reaches 23.1 seconds of arc. At the 1988 opposition the maximum apparent diameter will be slightly greater, at 23.7 seconds of arc, but all oppositions for the rest of the century will be much less favourable, and in 1995 the magnitude will not exceed −1, so that Mars will remain considerably fainter than Sirius.

Even small telescopes will show surface features on Mars this month, provided that seeing conditions are reasonably good. The main dark areas are to all intents and purposes permanent, though they show slight variations in extent and colour; the V-shaped Syrtis Major, in the southern hemisphere, was clearly drawn by Christiaan Huygens as long ago as 1659, and the polar caps were first recorded by G. D. Cassini in 1666. It was long claimed that when the polar caps shrink, in the Martian spring and early summer, the dark areas become more definite, as though they were due to organic material revived by moisture wafted from the caps by the Martian winds; but is is now known that the dark regions are not organic, and neither are they old sea-beds (the Syrtis Major is a lofty plateau). The so-called 'wave of darkening' seems to have been an optical illusion, as were the celebrated canals drawn so firmly by Percival Lowell and many others.

Mars rotates on its axis in a period of $24^h 37^m 22^s.6$. Thus a Martian day, or 'sol', is more than half an hour longer than ours. If the planet is observed on successive nights, it is easy to see that the markings are displaced, and the shifts can be noticed over periods of only a few minutes, though they are less pronounced than in the case of the larger and quicker-spinning Jupiter.

When observing Mars, it is desirable to use as high a magnification as is possible without losing sharp definition of the image. This means that telescopes of fair size are needed to show delicate details, and it must be admitted that to the owner of a small telescope (say a 76mm refractor) Mars is a much less rewarding object than Jupiter or Saturn. Moreover, it can be well seen for only a month or two to either side of opposition. During 1986 things are made worse, from the viewpoint of the Northern-Hemisphere observer, by the fact that Mars is in Sagittarius – about as far south as it can ever move, though, of course, this means that southern observers can see the planet almost overhead.

The two midget satellites, Phobos and Deimos, are not easy objects, and the best way to see them is to mask the image of Mars itself by an occulting disk; however, even this will not allow the satellites to be seen with any telescope of much under 30cm aperture. They are quite unlike our massive Moon, since they are irregular in shape; Phobos has a longest diameter of a mere 28 kilometres, while Deimos is even smaller. It is quite likely that both are ex-asteroids which were captured by Mars in the distant past, though admittedly this involves some special circumstances, and the theory has definite weaknesses.

VEGA. The lovely blue star Vega is now almost overhead during evenings in British latitudes. From Australia or South Africa it never rises high above the horizon, though it is obvious enough; observers in the southernmost part of New Zealand will be lucky to see it at all.

August

New Moon: August 5   *Full Moon:* August 19

Mercury is at greatest western elongation (19°) on August 11 and thus visible as a morning object. For Southern Hemisphere observers it is visible for all except the last few days of the month. For observers in the Northern Hemisphere this is the most suitable morning apparition of 1986, the visibility period being the middle two weeks of the month. Figure 6 shows, for observers in latitude N.52° the changes in azimuth (true bearing from the north through

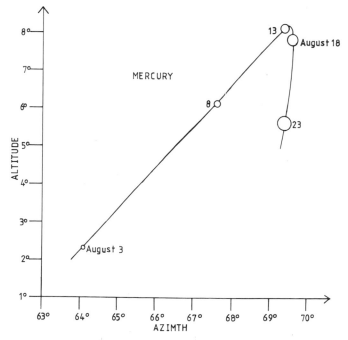

Figure 6. Morning apparition of Mercury for latitude N.52°.

east, south and west) and altitude of Mercury on successive mornings when the Sun is 6° below the horizon. At this time of year and in this latitude this condition, known as the beginning of morning civil twilight, occurs about 40 minutes before sunrise. The changes in the brightness of Mercury are indicated approximately by the sizes of the circles which mark its position at five-day intervals. It will be noticed that Mercury is brightest after it reaches greatest western elongation. On August 13 its magnitude is −0.1: ten days later it is −1.2.

Venus reaches greatest eastern elongation (46°) on August 27, with a magnitude of −3.9, and is thus a magnificent object in the western sky after sunset. The visibility conditions are quite different in the two hemispheres: whereas observers in latitude N.52° will only see the planet for an hour after sunset, those in latitude S.35° will find that Venus is setting over 3½ hours after sunset.

Mars continues to be visible as a brilliant object, visible for most of the night. It is still in Sagittarius, reaching its second stationary point on August 12.

Jupiter, magnitude −2.4, is a brilliant object and visible for the greater part of the night.

Saturn, magnitude +0.7, continues to be visible as an evening object.

HALLEY'S COMET. The comet is still in the region of Sextans and Crater, but it is in conjunction with the Sun this month and will be lost to view; before disappearing into the brightness of the sky, the magnitude will have dropped to about 9. The distance from Earth is now over 550,000,000 kilometres.

CENTENARY COMETS. Today, when comets are discovered so regularly, it may be of interest to look back to a time when only really bright visitors were likely to be detected. So what 'cometary centenaries' can we find?

The first seems to date back only three hundred years. (A comet had been seen a century earlier, in 1585, but it had been lost by the start of 1586.) The 1686 comet was discovered in August, from Brazil; the name of the actual discoverer is not known. On August

17 it was apparently very conspicuous, with an 18-degree tail and a nucleus as bright as a first-magnitude star; it was then at its closest to the Earth – only about 50,000,000 kilometres away. It faded slowly, and was still bright well into September; it was finally lost on September 22. The period must amount to many centuries.

1786 brought two discoveries. The first – and the most important, as subsequent events proved – was due to Pierre Méchain on January 17. (Méchain was a well-known French comet-hunter, and a friendly rival of Charles Messier, who was indefatigable in his searches and produced his catalogue of star-clusters and nebulæ to avoid wasting time on objects which were non-cometary.) Méchain's comet was of the fifth magnitude, and was in Aquarius. It was observed briefly; it was recovered in 1795 by Caroline Herschel, and again in 1805 by Pons. In 1818 Pons found it again, and an orbit was calculated by Johann Encke, who predicted its return for 1822. In that year it was duly picked up by C. L. Rümker, and it is now an old friend; we call it Encke's Comet, and it comes back every 3.3 years.

The other 1786 comet was discovered by Caroline Herschel on August 1. It reached naked-eye visibility, and developed a tail; it was followed until October 26. The period seems to be of the order of 9,000 years.

By 1886 comet-hunting had become fashionable, and nine comets were found during the year, of which three became visible without optical aid. The brightest of them was Barnard–Hartwig, found in Sextans in October. A long tail developed, and the maximum magnitude was around 3. It is apparently one of those comets to have been forced into a hyperbolic orbit by the perturbations of the planets, in which case it will never return.

THE PERSEIDS. The annual Perseid meteor shower is due in early August, and this year the Moon will not interfere until a late stage – well after the shower has reached its maximum intensity. The Perseids are very consistent, and, unlike the occasionally more spectacular Leonids, never fail to produce a rich shower. The associated comet is Swift–Tuttle, which has been seen at only one return, that of 1862, when it reached the second magnitude and produced a 30-degree tail. The period is uncertain. Calculations gave a value of 119.6 years, and the comet was expected back in 1981, but failed to materialize. Since then it has been suggested that Swift–Tuttle may be identical with Kogler's Comet of 1737, in which case the period is longer than had been expected, and the next perihelion will not take place until late 1992. Searches for it will be continued, though whether they will be successful remains to be seen.

September

New Moon: September 4   *Full Moon:* September 18

Equinox: September 23

Mercury passes through superior conjunction on September 5 and, for Southern Hemisphere observers, becomes visible as an evening object, low above the western horizon during the second half of the month (see Figure 7 with the notes for October).

Venus continues to be visible as a magnificent object in the western evening sky, magnitude −4.2. Sadly, for observers in northern temperate latitudes, the increase in its southern declination means that, for them, Venus is too close to the Sun for observation before the end of the month.

Mars continues to be visible in the south-western sky in the evenings. Mars has a magnitude of −1.

Jupiter reaches opposition on September 10, and is therefore visible throughout the hours of darkness. Its magnitude is −2.4. The path of the planet amongst the stars is shown in Figure 8 which is given with the notes for December. At opposition Jupiter is 592 million kilometres from the Earth.

Saturn, magnitude +0.8, is still visible as an evening object though observers in northern temperate latitudes will have difficulty in seeing Saturn for long after the end of the month.

CEPHEUS. Cepheus is a far-northern constellation. During September evenings it is almost overhead as seen from European latitudes, but most of it lies north of declination N.60°, so that it is to all intents and purposes inaccessible from Australia, South Africa and New Zealand.

It is not a really conspicuous group, but it contains some

interesting objects. The leading stars are Alpha or Alderamin (magnitude 2.4), Gamma or Alrai and Beta or Alphirk (3.2) and Zeta (3.5). Alphirk is a pulsating variable with a very small range; it has given its name to the whole class, though the Beta Cephei variables may also be know as Beta Canis Majoris variables. Zeta, with a K-type spectrum, is strongly orange in colour, and is at least 5,000 times as luminous as the Sun; its distance is over 700 light-years.

Delta Cephei makes up a small triangle with Zeta and the fainter Epsilon (magnitude 4.2). It is of course one of the most famous variables in the sky, and is the prototype Cepheid. The range is from magnitude 3.5 to 4.4, and the period is 5.4 days. The changes in brightness are easy to follow with the naked eye; Zeta and Epsilon make useful comparison stars, though Delta never becomes as bright as Zeta.

The constellation also contains Sir William Herschel's 'Garnet Star', Mu Cephei, which is undoubtedly the reddest of all the naked-eye stars. It has an M-type spectrum, and is very powerful indeed; it seems to be over 50,000 times as luminous as the Sun, in which case it is far more powerful than Betelgeux – though it is also much farther away; its distance is well over 1500 light-years. With binoculars it is striking, and has been likened to a glowing ember, but normally it is too faint for the colour to be well seen with the naked eye.

Mu Cephei is a variable star. Its range is from magnitude 3.6 to 5.1, but there is no firm evidence of a period. Various estimates have been given, one of which was 755 days, but there seems no doubt that even if this is valid – which is by no means certain – the behaviour is much more erratic than is the case with most semi-regular variables, and it is often said that it is one of the few genuinely irregular stars. A good comparison star is Nu Cephei, which is of type A and has a magnitude of 4.3. Nu and Mu are in the same low-power binocular field; Nu is exceptionally luminous, and may be the equal of 70,000 Suns, but it cannot be much less than 4000 light years away.

Also in this region of the sky is the huge eclipsing binary VV Cephei, with a period of 7430 days and a range of magnitude from 4.9 to 5.2. The next eclipse is not due until 1996. The primary is a red supergiant, and may be one of the largest stars known, with a diameter 1200 times that of the Sun – though this is naturally uncertain. The companion is a smaller, hot B9-type star.

Also in Cepheus are two more well-known variables, the intensely red Mira-type S Cephei (7.4 to 12.9; 488 days) and the semi-regular W Cephei (6.9 to 8.6, with a long period which is probably of the order of 1100 days). Close to Delta lies the binary system of Krüger 60, made up of two red dwarfs of exceptionally low luminosity – only 0.0004 that of the Sun in the case of the fainter component, Krüger 60B, which is also a flare star, and is otherwise known as DO Cephei. The revolution period of the two components is 44.5 years. A third star, 27 seconds of arc from the main pair, seems not to be a true member of the system.

Krüger 60 is one of the nearer stars, at a distance of 13 light-years. Its position is RA 22^h 26^m, declination N.57°27'. A relatively small telescope will show both components, and the change in position angle is easy to detect after only a few years. The real separation is, on average, about 9.2 astronomical units or almost 1400 million kilometres.

October

New Moon: October 3   *Full Moon:* October 17

Summer Time in Great Britain and Northern Ireland may end on October 12.

Mercury is an evening object throughout the month, though not for observers in northern temperate latitudes. This evening apparition is the most suitable one of the year for observers in southern latitudes. Figure 7 shows, for observers in latitude S.35°, the changes in azimuth and altitude of Mercury on successive evenings when the Sun is 6° below the horizon. At this time of year this condition, known as the end of evening civil twilight, occurs about 30 minutes after sunset. The changes in the brightness of the planet are roughly indicated by the sizes of the circles which mark its position at five-day intervals. It will be noticed that Mercury is brightest before it reaches greatest eastern elongation (24°), on October 21.

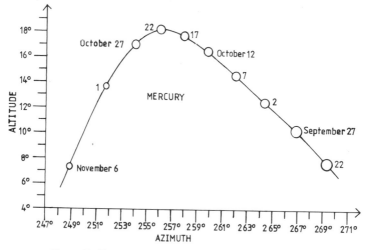

Figure 7. Evening apparition of Mercury for latitude S.35°.

Venus attains its greatest brilliancy (magnitude −4.6) on the first day of the month, though this spectacle will be denied to observers in northern temperate latitudes since for them Venus has disappeared in the evening twilight. For observers in the Southern Hemisphere Venus continues to be visible as a magnificent object dominating the western sky after sunset, though by the end of the month it is setting only about an hour after the Sun.

Mars is still visible in the evenings, in the south-western sky. It is now magnitude −0.5, two magnitudes fainter than when it was at opposition in July.

Jupiter, magnitude −2.3, continues to be visible for the greater part of the night.

Saturn is only visible for a short while in the early evenings.

HALLEY'S COMET. It will be almost impossible to see the comet this month. It is in Crater, but is inconveniently near the Sun in the sky.

THE ECLIPSE OF THE SUN. The solar eclipse of October 3 is unusual. For most of the central track it is annular, but over a very restricted area in the North Atlantic there will be a totality lasting for about one-tenth of a second! This certainly presents a challenge to any enthusiasts who are prepared to go to this particular region, which, perversely, is well away from dry land. It should be possible to see and photograph the corona if conditions are good, but certainly there will be no second chance. No more total solar eclipses will occur until March 18, 1988, when the maximum duration will be 3 minutes 46 seconds, and the central zone will extend over the Indian Ocean, the East Indies, and part of the Pacific.

ROBERT TRÜMPLER. This month's centenary is that of the Swiss astronomer Robert Julius Trümpler, who was born on October 2, in Zürich. He was the son of a businessman, and graduated from the University of Zürich, going on to Göttingen and gaining his PhD degree in 1910. He became interested in stellar proper motions, and a meeting with Frank Schlesinger, one of the pioneers in this field, led to an invitation to go to the Allegheny Observatory in Pennsylvania, where Schlesinger was Director. He stayed there until 1919, when he transferred to the Lick Observatory; in 1930 he was appointed Professor of Astronomy at the University of California, and remained there until retiring in 1951.

Trümpler carried out careful studies of the star-types in open clusters, notably the Pleiades, but perhaps his main contribution was his discovery, in 1930, that interstellar material was responsible for obscuring the light received from many galaxies. This had not been appreciated, and it had led to an over-estimation of the distances of the galaxies. While at the Lick Observatory he made observations of the planets, particularly Mars; he was unable to confirm the exsistence of the canals drawn by Schiaparelli and Lowell – it is now known that the canals do not exist; they were tricks of the eye.

Trümpler was twice President of the Astronomical Society of the Pacific, in 1932 and again in 1939. He died in Oakland, California, on September 10, 1956.

THE BEGINNING OF THE SPACE AGE. How many people attach any significance to October 4, 1957? Yet it was on this date that the Space Age was opened by the launching of Russia's first artificial satellite, Sputnik 1. Two years later Lunik 3 made a trip round the Moon, and sent back the first photographs of the far side which is always turned away from the Earth.

THE SQUARE OF PEGASUS. Pegasus, the Flying Horse, is marked by a pattern of four stars arranged in a square, though one of them, Alpheratz, has been transferred to the adjacent constellation of Andromeda as Alpha Andromedæ (it was formerly, and more logically, known as Delta Pegasi). The other stars in the main pattern are Beta Pegasi (variable; 2.4 to 2.8), Alpha (2.5) and Gamma (2.8, very slightly variable). The remaining bright star in Pegasus is Epsilon (2.4 which lies some way from the Square).

It is interesting to compare the apparent magnitudes of the four stars in the Square with their absolute magnitudes –that is to say, the apparent magnitudes which they would have if seen from a standard distance of 10 parsecs (32.6 light-years). Alpha Andromedæ would have a magnitude of −0.1; Beta Pegasi around −1.4; Alpha Pegasi 0.2; and Gamma Pegasi −3.0, so that although Gamma looks the fainest of the four it is in fact much the most luminous. Its distance from us is nearly 500 light-years.

November

Mercury is an evening object for the first week of the month (see Figure 7 with the notes for October), though not for observers in northern temperate latitudes. After passing through inferior conjunction on November 13 it becomes visible as a morning object for about the last ten days of the month, low above the south-east horizon at the time of beginning of morning civil twilight.

At inferior conjunction on November 13 Mercury will be seen in transit across the face of the Sun, for observers in Australasia, Asia, Antarctica, Africa (except the north-west), and eastern Europe.

Venus is not visible at first, as it passes through inferior conjunction on November 5. It rapidly moves away from the Sun and by the middle of the month has become visible low above the south-eastern horizon before sunrise.

Mars, magnitude +0.1, moves from Capricornus into Aquarius during November. It continues to be visible in the south-western sky in the evenings.

Jupiter is an evening object in the south and south-western sky. Jupiter is in Aquarius and has a magnitude of −2.2.

Saturn, already lost to view for observers in the Northern Hemisphere, is a difficult object for those in the Southern Hemisphere, fading into the twilight by the middle of the month.

THE TRANSIT OF MERCURY. This month's transit of Mercury is the first since 1973. There will be only two more before the end of the century: on November 16, 1993 and November 15, 1999 (transits can only occur in May and November).

The twelfth-century Arab astronomer Alpetragius commented that he had never seen Mercury pass across the face of the Sun, and from this concluded that the planet must be self-luminous! The first prediction of a transit was made by Kepler, who found that the phenomenon would occur on November 7, 1631; it did so, and was observed by Pierre Gassendi. The transit of November 8, 1644 passed unobserved; that of November 2, 1651 was seen by Shakerley from India; that of November 4, 1664 was missed, but Edmond Halley saw the next, on November 7, 1677, from the island of St. Helena, where he had gone to make pioneer observations of the southern stars. Since then all transits have been observed except those of 1707 and 1710. During the present century there have been transits in 1907, 1914, 1924, 1927, 1937, 1940, 1953, 1957, 1960, 1970 and 1973. The transit takes some time – several hours, in fact.

Halley suggested that transits of Mercury might be used in attempts to measure the length of the astronomical unit, or distance between the Earth and the Sun. His method was sound enough in principle, and was actually put into practice with transits of Venus. At such times Venus is clearly visible with the naked eye, whereas Mercury is too small. However, the method depends upon timing the exact moments of ingress and egress, and with Venus this was impossible because of an effect known as the Black Drop; as Venus passes on to the solar disk it seems to draw a strip of blackness after it, and when this disappears the transit has already begun. The results from the last two transits of Venus, those of 1874 and 1882, were not satisfactory, and the method is obsolete, so that the next transit of Venus, in 2004, will be regarded as of no real importance.

Transits of Mercury are interesting to watch. The planet has virtually no atmosphere, and no Black Drop would be expected, though at the 1927 transit the effect was recorded by E. M. Antoniadi, the leading planetary observer of the period, who was using the 83cm refractor at the Meudon Observatory, Paris.

Various other effects have been recorded at transits. A greyish halo round the disk was noted by Schröter, Harding and Schumacher during early nineteenth century transits, but there is no doubt that this was due to instrumental defects, and the same is true of the bright aureole reported by Reboul in 1907. In his book *The Planet Mercury*[1], Antoniadi listed cases of luminous patches seen on

---

1. Published in French in 1934. It did not appear in English until 1974, when I produced a translation – but by then Mariner 10 had by-passed the planet, so that Antoniadi's book was of historical interest only!

the disk during transit. There were a surprising number of such reports, ranging from stationary bright patches to irregular streaks and even moving spots. In view of what we now know about Mercury, there seems no escape from the conclusion that all these records were illusory.

There is, however, one interesting observation to be made. If there are any sunspots on the disk, compare them with the blackness of the disk of Mercury. It is obvious at a glance that Mercury is much the darker. Sunspots are not black at all; they are at a temperature of about 2000 degrees lower than that of the bright surrounding surface or photosphere, so that they appear dark by contrast. If they could be seen shining on their own, their surface brightness would be greater than that of an arc-lamp, whereas Mercury is truly black. If any sunspots are on view on November 13 this year, the effect will be striking. It is unfortunate that the transit occurs round 4 hours G.M.T., so that it will not be visible from Britain, but it should be well seen from South Africa and Australasia.

December

New Moon: December 1, 31   Full Moon: December 16

Solstice: December 22

Mercury continues to be visible as a morning object for the first two weeks of the month (and slightly longer for observers in the Southern Hemisphere). It may be glimpsed low above the south-eastern horizon at the time of beginning of morning civil twilight. Its magnitude will be −0.6.

Venus is a brilliant object, attaining greatest brilliancy (magnitude −4.7) on December 11. It dominates the south-eastern sky for several hours before dawn. Have you ever seen Venus in daylight? A good opportunity for doing so occurs on the morning of December 28 when observers could use the old crescent Moon as a guide. The Moon passes 7° S. of Venus at 01^h G.M.T. on that day (remember that the Moon moves at an angular speed roughly equivalent to its own diameter every hour).

Mars is still visible as an evening object in the south-western sky. Its path amongst the stars is shown in Figure 8. On December 19 Mars passes only ½° N. of Jupiter.

Jupiter, magnitude −2.0, continues to be visible as an evening object in the south and south-western sky. Figure 8 shows its path amongst the stars.

Saturn passes through conjunction on December 4 and remains unobservable for those in the Northern Hemisphere. By the end of the month observers in the Southern Hemisphere may be able to glimpse it low above the south-eastern horizon before morning twilight inhibits observation.

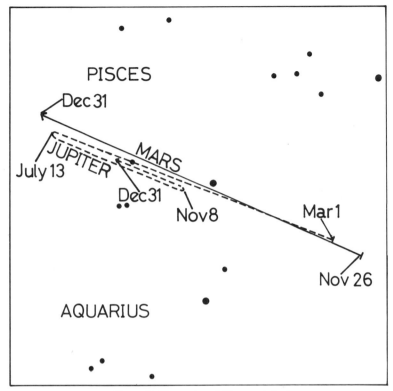

Figure 8. The paths of Mars and Jupiter.

HALLEY'S COMET. The comet is still in Crater, and will in fact remain there through 1987; its apparent motion has become very slow, and the distance from Earth has now increased to well over 6,000,000 kilometres. It is fading to such an extent that it is now beyond the reach of any but large telescopes. It may well be followed until 1989 or 1990, but then we will lose it. It next reaches aphelion in the year 2024, and will not be recovered until the 2050s. So for most of us it is time to say farewell to Halley's Comet. It has provided us with a tremendous amount of interest and excitement; I think that everyone will be sorry to see it depart!

RED ACHERNAR? Achernar or Alpha Eridani, the 'Last in the River', lies in the far south of the sky. Its declination is S.57°, so that it is never visible from the latitudes of Britain or North America; it is in fact the nearest really brilliant star to the south celestial pole. Its apparent magnitude is 0.46, so that it is the ninth brightest star in the sky, and it is 780 times as luminous as the Sun; its distance is 85 light-years.

Achernar is of spectral type B5, so that it is white, perhaps slightly bluish. Yet in a catalogue produced in the 1890s, G. F. Chambers describes it as red! There can be no possibility of real change; Achernar is simply not that kind of star, and there is no doubt that Chambers' catalogue is wrong. Yet the mistake is so obvious that one must cast around for an explanation. (It is not a simple misprint, as the colour is described as red in several other catalogues produced at about the same time.)

It is, of course, true that at that period most astronomical books were written by observers living in the Northern Hemisphere, so that they could never see Achernar; and it is a sad fact that once an error is made, it tends to be perpetuated unless careful checks are made. This must surely be the answer. On the other hand, we must note that there are several other instances of stars whose colours have been wrongly reported.

The classic case is that of Sirius, which was described by Ptolemy (circa A.D. 150) and other astronomers of ancient times as being red, whereas it is in fact pure white – though when seen low down it does twinkle violently and flash various colours, due entirely to the effects of the Earth's atmosphere. There has been great discussion about the alleged colour-change in Sirius. One suggestion was that the faint companion Sirius B, now a White Dwarf, used to be a red giant two thousand years ago; but this idea is completely out of court, because the time-scale is completely wrong, and in addition the present Sirius combined with a red giant companion would make a star of quite improbable brilliancy. It has been claimed that the evidence in favour of change is conclusive; but the case of Achernar is an extra pointer to the fallacy of this suggestion.

There is no certain case of a colour-change in a normal star, though it is true that some variables show different degrees of redness during their cycles (particularly with Mira stars). Incidentally, the only naked-eye star which is said to be greenish is Beta Libræ. Few people will see any colour at all in it, however, and I have never met anyone who describes it as green, so that again we seem to be dealing with an initial mistake which has been repeated time and time again. It is never wise to take anything on trust – particularly in astronomy!

Eclipses in 1986

In 1986 there will be two eclipses of the Sun and two of the Moon.

(1) *A partial eclipse of the Sun on April 9* is visible from the south-eastern part of Indonesia, Australia, New Guinea, South Island of New Zealand, the southern part of the Indian Ocean, and part of Antarctica. The eclipse begins at 04^h 10^m and ends at 08^h 32^m. At the time of maximum eclipse 0.82 of the Sun's diameter is obscured.

(2) *A total eclipse of the Moon on April 24* is visible from the western part of North America, the Pacific Ocean, Antarctica, Australasia, Indonesia, the Philippine Islands, Japan, the eastern part of Asia, and the eastern part of the Indian Ocean. The eclipse begins at 11^h 04^m and ends at 14^h 22^m. Totality lasts from 12^h 11^m to 13^h 15^m.

(3) *An annular-total eclipse of the Sun on October 3.* The path of the annular-total phase begins between Greenland and Iceland and ends to the south of Iceland. The partial phase is visible from the extreme north-eastern part of Asia, North America except the extreme south-western part, the Arctic regions, Greenland, Iceland, the North Atlantic Ocean except the eastern part, and the northern part of South America. The eclipse begins at 16^h 57^m and ends at 21^h 13^m; the annular phase begins at 18^h 56^m and ends at 19^h 15^m; the total phase begins at 19^h 05^m and ends at 19^h 08^m. The maximum duration of the annular phase is $2^s.6$; the maximum duration of the total phase is $0^s.3$.

(4) *A total eclipse of the Moon on October 17* is visible from Australia, New Guinea, Indonesia, the Philippine Islands,

Japan, Asia, the Indian Ocean, Africa, Europe (including the British Isles), the eastern part of the Atlantic Ocean, Iceland, the eastern part of Greenland, and the Arctic regions. The eclipse begins at $17^h 30^m$ and ends at $21^h 06^m$. Totality lasts from $18^h 41^m$ to $19^h 55^m$.

TRANSIT OF MERCURY IN 1986

Mercury will transit the disk of the Sun on November 13. It will be visible from Australasia, Asia, part of Antarctica, Africa (except the north-west), and eastern Europe. It will commence at $01^h 43^m$ and end at $06^h 31^m$. It will take approximately two minutes for the disk of Mercury to move fully on to or off, the disk of the Sun.

Occultations in 1986

In the course of its journey round the sky each month, the Moon passes in front of all the stars in its path and the timing of these occultations is useful in fixing the position and motion of the Moon. The Moon's orbit is tilted at more than five degrees to the ecliptic, but it is not fixed in space. It twists steadily westwards at a rate of about twenty degrees a year, a complete revolution taking 18.6 years, during which time all the stars that lie within about six and a half degrees of the ecliptic will be occulted. The occultations of any one star continue month after month until the Moon's path has twisted away from the star but only a few of these occultations will be visible at any one place in hours of darkness.

There are six occultations of planets in 1986, two of Mercury and four of Mars. None of these is visible from either Great Britain or North America.

Only four first-magnitude stars are near enough to the ecliptic to be occulted by the Moon; these are Regulus, Aldebaran, Spica, and Antares. Of these four only Antares is occulted in 1986. It is occulted once during each lunation from March 30 to December 29.

Predictions of these occultations are made on a world-wide basis for all stars down to magnitude 7.5, and sometimes even fainter. Lunar occultations of radio sources are also of interest – remember the first quasar, 3C.273, was discovered as the result of an occultation.

Recently occultations of stars by planets (including minor planets) and satellites have aroused considerable attention.

The exact timing of such events gives valuable information about positions, sizes, orbits, atmospheres and sometimes of the presence of satellites. The discovery of the rings of Uranus in 1977 was the unexpected result of the observations made of a predicted occultation of a faint star by Uranus. The duration of an occultation by a satellite or minor planet is quite small (usually of the order of a minute or less). If observations are made from a number of stations it is possible to deduce the size of the planet.

The observations need to be made either photoelectrically or visually. The high accuracy of the method can readily be appreciated when one realizes that even a stop-watch timing accurate to $0^s.1$ is, on average, equivalent to an accuracy of about 1 kilometre in the chord measured across the minor planet.

Comets in 1986

The appearance of a bright comet is a rare event which can never be predicted in advance, because this class of object travels round the Sun in an enormous orbit with a period which may well be many thousands of years. There are therefore no records of the previous appearances of these bodies, and we are unable to follow their wanderings through space.

Comets of short period, on the other hand, return at regular intervals, and attract a good deal of attention from astronomers. Unfortunately they are all faint objects, and are recovered and followed by photographic methods using large telescopes. Most of these short-period comets travel in orbits of small inclination which reach out to the orbit of Jupiter, and it is this planet which is mainly responsible for the severe perturbations which many of these comets undergo. Unlike the planets, comets may be seen in any part of the sky, but since their distances from the Earth are similar to those of the planets their apparent movements in the sky are also somewhat similar, and some of them may be followed for long periods of time.

The following periodic comets are expected to return to perihelion in 1986:

Comet	Year of Discovery	Period (years)	Date of predicted perihelion 1986
Boethin	1975	11.2	Jan. 19
Ashbrook-Jackson	1948	7.5	Jan. 24
Halley	–	76.0	Feb. 9
Holmes	1892	7.1	Mar. 14
Wirtanen	1948	5.5	Mar. 19
Kojima	1970	7.9	Apr. 4
Whipple	1933	8.5	June 25

Minor Planets in 1986

Although many thousands of minor planets (asteroids) are known to exist, only 3,000 of these have well-determined orbits and are listed in the catalogues. Most of these orbits lie entirely between the orbits of Mars and Jupiter. All of these bodies are quite small, and even the largest, Ceres, is believed to be only about 1,000 kilometres in diameter. Thus, they are necessarily faint objects, and although a number of them are within the reach of a small telescope few of them ever reach any considerable brightness. The first four that were discovered are named Ceres, Pallas, Juno and Vesta. Actually the largest four minor planets are Ceres, Pallas, Vesta and Hygiea. Vesta can occasionally be seen with the naked eye and this is most likely to occur when an opposition occurs near June, since Vesta would then be at perihelion. In 1986 Ceres will be at opposition on February 27 (magnitude 6.8), Juno on May 30 (magnitude 10.3) and Vesta on October 3 (magnitude 6.4).

A vigorous campaign for observing the occultations of stars by the minor planets has produced improved values for the dimensions of some of them, as well as the suggestion that some of these planets may be accompanied by satellites. Many of these observations have been made photoelectrically. However, amateur observers have found renewed interest in the minor planets since it has been shown that their visual timings of an occultation of a star by minor planet are accurate enough to lead to reliable determinations of diameter (see page 117). As a consequence many groups of observers all over the world are now organizing themselves for expeditions should the predicted track of such an occultation cross their country.

In 1984 the British Astronomical Association formed a special Minor Planet Section.

Meteors in 1986

Meteors ('shooting stars') may be seen on any clear moonless night, but on certain nights of the year their number increases noticeably. This occurs when the Earth chances to intersect a concentration of meteoric dust moving in an orbit around the Sun. If the dust is well spread out in space, the resulting shower of meteors may last for several days. The word 'shower' must not be misinterpreted – only on very rare occasions have the meteors been so numerous as to resemble snowflakes falling.

If the meteor tracks are marked on a star map and traced backwards, a number of them will be found to intersect in a point (or a small area of the sky) which marks the radiant of the shower. This gives the direction from which the meteors have come.

The following table gives some of the more easily observed showers with their radiants; interference by moonlight is shown by the letter M.

Limiting dates	Shower	Maximum	R.A.	Dec.	
Jan.1-6	Quadrantids	Jan. 4	15^h28^m	$+50°$	M
Mar. 14-18	Arids	Mar. 16	16^h20^m	$-48°$	
April 20-22	Lyrids	April 21	18^h08^m	$+32°$	M
May 1-8	Aquarids	May 5	22^h20^m	$+00°$	
June 17-26	Ophiuchids	June 19	17^h20^m	$-20°$	M
July 15-Aug. 15	Delta Aquarids	July 27	22^h36^m	$-17°$	M
July 15-Aug. 20	Pisces Australids	July 31	22^h40^m	$-30°$	
July 15-Aug. 25	Capricornids	Aug. 1	20^h36^m	$-10°$	
July 27-Aug. 17	Perseids	Aug. 12	3^h04^m	$+58°$	
Oct. 15-25	Orionids	Oct. 21	6^h24^m	$+15°$	M
Oct. 26-Nov. 16	Taurids	Nov. 7	3^h44^m	$+14°$	
Nov. 15-19	Leonids	Nov. 17	10^h08^m	$+22°$	M
Dec. 9-14	Geminids	Dec. 14	7^h28^m	$+32°$	M
Dec. 17-24	Ursids	Dec. 23	14^h28^m	$+78°$	M

M=moonlight interferes

Some Events in 1987

ECLIPSES

In 1987 there will two eclipses, both of the Sun.

March 29: annular-total eclipse of the Sun – southern part of South America, Antarctica, Africa, extreme south-eastern Europe, south-west Asia.

September 23: annular eclipse of the Sun – Asia, Australasia.

THE PLANETS

Mercury may be seen more easily from northern latitudes in the evenings about the time of greatest eastern elongation (February 12) and in the mornings around greatest western elongation (July 25). In the Southern Hemisphere the corresponding dates are March 26 (mornings) and October 4 (evenings).

Venus is visible in the mornings until July and in the evenings from October onwards.

Mars is an evening object for the first half of the year and in the mornings from November onwards.

Jupiter is at opposition on October 18.

Saturn is at opposition on June 9.

Uranus is at opposition on June 16.

Neptune is at opposition on June 28.

Pluto is at opposition on April 29.

PART TWO

Article Section

DAVID ALLEN

Australian Pepper: extraterrestrial débris

Australia: a place of contrast, of sun and storm, of desert and forest; an untamed land.

So vast is this island continent one requires a lifetime to explore its idiosyncracies. During a decade of Land Rover travel, Carol and I have merely scratched a few winding trails across its sandy surface, tasting the outback haphazardly. We know no more of Australia than the visitor to London who ventures only a few hundred yards from each of a dozen underground stations. Yet even that sketchy sample has enriched our lives with a thousand gems, with experiences foreign to the city dweller, with memories we will cherish when our expedition years are behind us. A few of these memories I share now, memories which I hope will convey at least a morsel of the enjoyment one can have pursuing astronomical interests in so wonderful a land.

More than any place I know, the inland of Australia has been sandpapered by time. Nowhere does the land exceed 2500 metres in elevation, and if one restricts the discussion to the inland basin beyond the littoral ranges of subdued hills, half that figure is appropriate. You can drive for a day and see no elevation greater that that of the telegraph poles that resolutely course from one town to the next. The summer rains that land in Queensland take a year to flow to the sea, if they even make it that far, following waterways that descend only a few inches in every mile. Floods in the inland are not torrential affairs: the water level in the Darling may take weeks to rise, seep over its banks and laboriously spread across the countryside, and then recede with similar lethargy. You can boil a billy of bush tea and be on to your second cup in the time it takes a twig to drift by at the height of the flood.

The leisurely pace of the outback is reflected in the erosion. The landscape scarcely changes in a lifetime, save where man in his greed has overstocked the grazing land, and from where now the precious topsoil blows unhindered into the Tasman sea, sometimes causing excessive extinction at Siding Spring Observatory as it passes. Even on the timescale geologists use, Australia doesn't alter appreciably. Should you blast a crater into an atomic test range today, it would testify several generations hence to your delinquency. Equally, where Nature herself blasted craters into the desert tens of aeons ago, their scars remain today to delight the curious. A continent so vast must have been peppered by extraterrestrial débris; it is some of these sites I now describe.

It seems appropriate to do so in 1986 when the world is toasting once again that remarkable Englishman, Edmond Halley. We think of Halley because of his comet, ignoring his impact in so many other fields of science. This is not the place to eulogize Halley's numerous achievements, but it is fitting to note that he provided the first reasoned arguments that rocks can and do land on Earth from outer space. True, there had been a school of thought in ancient Greece favouring this proposition, but its proponents could do no more than handwave in support of their tenet. Like so many astronomical theories now known to be correct, this was overwhelmed by the clumsy but popular philosophy of Aristotle. Halley probably had read the earlier Greek works, being fluent in ancient Greek, but his arguments were new, scientific and incontrovertible. Unfortunately, Halley was ahead of his time: a century was to pass before he was believed.

Small rocks pepper the Earth quite frequently. Unless seen to fall, they are rarely discovered because most resemble terrestrial stones. In our travels through Australia we probably saw many meteorites, as such nomads are called, but like all before us we would not have recognized the fact. Only the big specimens attract attention, and then usually only if they have a distinctive mineralogy. Some meteorites are made of iron, and these in particular are relatively easy to find.

The best collection of meteorites in the continent lies in the Perth museum, in Western Australia. I particularly wanted to see the largest specimen known in the country, the Mundrabilla meteorite. My interest in it has been raised, appropriately enough, by an article in the *1969 Yearbook of Astronomy* written by the man who brought it back, Dr Jo McCall. That article had described the difficulty of finding the meteorite even with foreknowledge of its approximate location. Now, one can easily imagine the difficulty of spotting a large lump of rock in the Coolins of Skye, or deep in the Amazon rain forests, but Jo McCall had had to hunt on the famous Nullarbor Plain, a treeless expanse of billowing moorland in which no piece of vegetation stands half as high as the rock itself. Somehow McCall's narrative rang hollow. How could one encounter such trouble, I asked myself. I had to find out.

The first realization came when I saw the meteorite itself. From the photographs, I had thought it at least as tall as a man. In retrospect I have the feeling I even pictured something half the size of a house. No – the Mundrabilla meteorite would have fitted quite comfortably under your dining table . . . and that was the larger of the two pieces recovered! But the real immensity of the task of finding this rock could be appreciated only by having a look at Mundrabilla too.

You reach Mundrabilla on the Eyre Highway, a narrow pencil line of bitumen fashioned across the western half of Australia. Arriving from the east we spent a night in the pleasant little resort of Ceduna, in South Australia, before embarking on the two-day journey to the next town, the mining establishment of Norseman, a little south of Kalgoorlie. The Nullarbor Plain contains no towns, no villages. Ceduna is on a time zone nine and a half hours ahead of Greenwich. Odd half hours on time zones always seem contrived to me, the more so since Adelaide, the major city in the zone, actually lies closer to nine hours ahead of Greenwich in longitude. Norseman, like Perth, is eight hours ahead. You might imagine that a ninety minute time change could be easily lost in the incomprehensible vastness of the Nullarbor; but no! A handful of farmsteads lies dotted along the Eyre Highway, and by common consent these have decided to adopt their own local time, midway between the western and southern ones. Mundrabilla is one of these farmsteads, eight hours and forty-five minutes ahead of Greenwich.

The farmhouse has expanded its activities to accommodate the many travellers who pass its doors. We pitched our tent in a dusty campground next to the shop and garage, just a few paces from the highway. Beneath a starry sky we slept to the sounds of a diesel generator and passing vehicles.

The Nullarbor Plain is awesome. It is just so big and empty. To relieve the motorist a series of road signs has been erected:

kangaroos for next 500 km; beware camels crossing; etc. Because the road follows close to the coastline of the Australian Bight, there are some trees – just sufficient to make you wonder whether in fact 'Nullarbor' is the name of a local tribe of Aborigines rather than the last outpost of the Roman empire. A little way inland, however, there are no trees at all; instead the eye rests on an ocean of passing salt bushes and other tough shrubs whose wave crests reach little more than knee high.

The entire central swath of the continent is a massive natural barrier, so much so that the wildlife is almost totally different on the two sides of Australia. Only a few reptiles and the birds of prey that feed on them bridge the Nullarbor and so are common to the east and west; oh, and those damned bush flies. One can set to wondering whether man himself has any place venturing across this barrier, at least by surface routes. The artificiality of that pencil line is luringly comforting.

To experience the true Nullarbor, we drove off the Eyre Highway along a track to one of the limestone caverns that dot the plain. With the throb of the highway out of earshot we were able to come to grips with the Nullarbor. Suddenly we became a microscopic speck in the emptiness. The Nullarbor Plain expanded tenfold and more in our perception. We began to appreciate the enormity of McCall's task.

There was something wonderful about tracking across the big sky country. Apart from the wheel ruts ahead of us, there was no hint that man had been here before us. We could savour the explorations of Eyre himself, and of the indomitable Ernest Giles, men who would travel for days on end through changeless scenery hoping, praying that a water hole would be found before it was too late.

What was most striking about this small détour was the return to the highway. We meandered back along the same wheel ruts for what seemed like twice the distance we had first traversed. A slight uneasiness began to creep over us that we had somehow gone astray and were now following the wrong set of tracks. Common sense had difficulty in overcoming this concern even though it was perfectly obvious that we could not fail to join the bitumen road if we kept the sun to our backs. And join it we did. It so happened that no vehicles lay in sight on the Eyre Highway as we approached it. As a result, we failed to spot the road until we lay within a mere few paces of it. Dramatically, the road appeared from amongst the saltbush stands just beyond our front wheels, concealed to the last. In the distance we could see a receding car which would have passed by when we were but a few hundred yards from the road. A car considerably larger than the Mundrabilla meteorite, a moving object, something we had been watching intently for, but something we had failed to see. I realized there and then that, even had we been equipped with maps of the calibre of the Ordnance Survey's old 6-inch-to-the-mile series, we would have stood no chance at all of finding the Mundrabilla meteorite. Suddenly I identified with Jo McCall's task.

Equally difficult to find are the tektites so liberally strewn across Australia. Tektites are glassy objects, dark and small, and exist in numbers uncountable. Virtually the entire continent has fields of tektites, particularly the southern portions. They are light in weight and have thus tended to be washed to lake shores. The lakes of Australia were once very numerous, but the desiccation of the continent that followed the ice age shrunk their numbers a thousandfold. Many dry lake sites dot the inland, identifiable by their flat sandy beds, and it is around these that the fossicker is recommended to look for tektites. We never found any, but perhaps we have always been too busy travelling to spend long enough looking. The Aborigines, who regarded tektites as sacred stones, are notoriously good at grubbing them out of apparently stone-free country. Many of the tektites in Australia undoubtedly lie buried by a few inches of windblown sand.

The tektites fell about 750,000 years ago, though the date is rather uncertain, and recent evidence suggests that two falls were involved, separated by 140,000 years. Clearly distinct from normal meteorites, tektites show evidence of having been molten on production and subsequently of a further melt as they penetrated the Earth's atmosphere. Their distribution, in fewer than ten locations for falls over the last 35 million years, suggests that the falls are sudden, widespread, but extremely rare events. The Australian tektites are the youngest known. The fall included parts of south-east Asia. The chemical composition of tektites differs significantly from that of the surrounding land, as would be expected for something of extraterrestrial origin. It was long argued that they resulted from an impact or catastrophic volcanic event on the Moon, such that a cloud of tektites was flung Earthwards. Now we know the chemical composition of many bits of the Moon, we can see little similarity to that of tektites. Until we have sampled more of that body the argument cannot be overwhelming, but it has focused attention back to the Earth, and it is now widely believed that a giant terrestrial impact was responsible for their original melting. The molten blobs must have soared high above the Earth's surface, and cooled before plunging back once again on to a completely different part of the globe. The origin of the Australian tektite field is not determined. A crater in Kampuchea has been suggested.

Tektites are small objects that might hurt if they hit you but do no more than pock the sand where they fall, and even the Mundrabilla meteorite created only a small hollow around its base. Bigger objects striking the Earth, though much rarer occurrences, leave big craters but usually obliterate themselves in the act. There are three major craters in Australia, and two of these we have now visited. The third, Wolf Creek crater, lies in the north-west about as remote from our base in Sydney as it is possible to imagine; it may be some time before we venture that far. The other two are surprisingly close together, near the centre of the continent.

Our journey to the centre of Australia occupied five weeks. We crossed the southern plains to Adelaide, enjoying the green of Victoria as a contrast to the red centre that would follow. Northwards from Adelaide we soon forsook paved road for the rugged sand of the Stuart Highway. This famous road, the only line sketched through the middle of the continent, led us past Woomera, the rocket-launching site of fame named after the aboriginal spear thrower, and on to Coober Pedy. We spent a night in the campground at Coober Pedy, wondering all along whether we had inadvertently pitched our tent in the main street. There is neither grass nor tarmac in Coober Pedy, and the only feature that distinguished the campground from any other patch of the town was the litter of bent tent pegs.

Beneath this rock-hard surface lies a subterranean warren of opal mines. Most inhabitants live in forsaken mines, homes which can be quite comfortable once you have got used to the dank, earthy smell, but which would leave us desperate for daylight. The mining of opals is a deadly serious business here, a law unto itself. In the dead of night some tour the spoil heaps with ultraviolet lamps seeking pieces of opal missed in the dim light underground, but woe betide those who are caught by the owners.

The road north from Coober Pedy worsened, if that is possible. With the passage of many tyres the gravel and sand is piled into corrugations – solid waves which rise several inches to rounded crests, marching in regular array for miles along the road. Graders battle to smooth this ocean of stone, but are so outnumbered by traffic as to make little impact on the problem. The peaks of the wave pattern lie about one pace apart. Travelling at low speed along the road the Land Rover was pitched violently with every crest topped, shaking vehicle and contents alike. No vehicle could stand the many hundreds of miles of that sort of treatment that the Stuart Highway offers; to overcome it we had to travel fast: 43 miles per hour was the critical speed; below that we tossed about like a boat in a storm whereas above that speed the suspension (what was left of it) handled the corrugations, converting them into a continuous vibration. I sat at times in the passenger seat watching screws slowly vibrate loose and fall out. Carol would force the vehicle up to speed, make a few hundred yards, then come upon a smooth patch. We soon learnt to recognize these smooth patches for what they were: huge potholes filled with fine sand (bull dust, the locals call it). With a dull thud the Land Rover would sink into the sand, wallow heavily in it as its momentum was slowly destroyed, then crash into the far edge of the pothole. The front of the vehicle would buck violently into the air, shortly to be followed by the rear. The result of each pothole was to slow the vehicle well below the critical speed, so we next had to force the poor creature back up to 43 mph, in readiness for the next pothole.

The inhabitants of Coober Pedy do a roaring trade in vehicle repairs and have no wish to see their road improved.

Nor did the scenery in that part of South Australia offer much compensation. Mile after mile we crossed the gibber plains. Gibbers (with a hard 'g') are small, flat stones polished a glossy, rich brown by the action of sun, wind and sand. They are of great antiquity: turn over a gibber and its paler undersurface will be prominent for centuries. Every few dozen paces a tuft of hardy grass or a tiny grey plant defiantly pokes its way through the gibbers, complete with its slight drift of windborne sand that gives it some hope of nourishment. Incredibly, this is grazing land. The stations are large and the cattle lean. On average about six inches of rain falls per year here, though there can be several consecutive years with none at all. The harsh sun could evaporate away a

Figure 1. Three tektites from the Australia/S.E. Asia fall. The largest is about 6cm long. The smallest shows the smooth interior of a bubble that formed in a larger parent body.

Figure 2. A view into one of the Henbury meteorite craters from a point on a common rim. The crater floor is marked by the richer vegetation, including trees.

six-inch-deep puddle in a day. There are only two kinds of plants here – the quick and the dead.

The miles limped by. Ahead, nearer to Alice Springs, we knew the road to be paved, and we counted down the distance longingly. To our unending relief we found the newly paved road to have advanced to meet us. As we crossed the border from South Australia to the Northern Territories, a transformation came over us. Suddenly there was quiet, comfort. Only the gasping of the poor vehicle persisted to remind us of the ordeal behind (various bits had broken or fallen off by this stage). Suddenly, too, the landscape had become transformed into one of great beauty. The gibber plains made way for low hills with bare craggy crests. Trees stood by the roadside and an incredible, rich, ochre sand piled here and there into shapely dunes. Carpeting much of the ground were stands of gourds, paddy melons as they are locally known. These have sprouted from the seeds that filled the saddles of the many Afghan camels that have trodden the route between Alice Springs and civilization. Indeed, the former rail line that eventually replaced the camel trains was affectionately known as the 'Ghan' in remembrance of them.

The paved road led directly to Alice Springs, but a few hours before the town we turned left at a prominent sign directing us to the Henbury meteorite craters. Only a short drive along an uncannily smooth dirt road took us to a spacious parking area, and from there we set off on foot.

One might be forgiven for walking right past the Henbury craters without seeing them. Those who expect deep holes in the ground will certainly be surprised. The Henbury meteorite fragmented before it landed, and more than a dozen pieces were large enough to have formed recognizable craters; but none of the craters exceeds a few hundred paces across, and the deepest depression remaining now is not much greater than the height of a man. The craters jostle together for a share of this stretch of desert, and in most cases low ridges are common to two adjacent craters. One may amble along these ridges, with shallow hollows on both sides, and in a few minutes visit every crater. Once we had surveyed the lie of the land, we became aware also of the differences of vegetation between the interiors of these craters and the dusty plain in which they sit. The floors of the craters are quite flat, but gently sloping sides must feed to them an excess of the occasional rains, for the growth of plants and low trees is considerably more prominent within. As throughout most of the inland of Australia, the vegetation is extremely pastel in hue, its subtle colours blending with the pale gravel and sand.

We spent a couple of days in The Alice, repairing the Land Rover and ourselves, stocking up on provisions. Then we were off once more, westwards to adventure.

The central region of Australia, particularly just to the west of Alice Springs, is a fascinating area; I could easily fill this book with tales of our travels. But I must restrain my eager fingers and restrict the descriptions to Gosse's Bluff.

Maps of the region are notoriously bad. We followed narrow tracks that bore little resemblance to the maps we carried, and I became quite convinced that we were on the wrong route. I sought a small crater, but could see none between us and an abrupt range of hills in the near distance. Meeting another vehicle, we asked if they knew where Gosse's Bluff lay. 'That's it', the driver responded, pointing to the little range.

The track led straight up to the massif of hills which now towered impregnable above us. Then, unexpectedly, there appeared a rift, a doorway that led us through the walls and into the level interior as if through a secret passage. Here we were, driving across the bottom of a huge crater, completely surrounded by high ramparts. The low sun picked out the eastern rim and sent long shadows spilling from the western walls on to an undulating floor. We drove to a spot somewhere near the middle and pitched our tent. We were alone in the crater. 'I hope it doesn't strike twice in the same spot' said Carol.

Morning came clear but cold. In thick sweaters we broke camp and set off to explore the walls. We found a place where we could gain the rim for a better view. A lone rock wallaby, disturbed by our clatter, sprinted up a steeply tilted rock face with apparent ease. We laboured over rough terrain until we attained the almost level rim of the crater, perhaps 500 feet above the inner floor and the outer plain.

From this spot we could make out the circular shape very clearly. Most of the walls were continuous, but near at hand lay a section where the natural stratification had caused the walls to split into three parallel sections, and it was through breaks in the parallel sections that the track we had followed last night entered the compound. The stratification of the rock could be seen elsewhere on the sunlit portions of the walls, tilted steeply upwards presumably by the blast that formed Gosse's Bluff.

Gosse himself was something of an explorer, though he did not travel as far as the better-known men. With his Afghan camel driver, Gosse covered much of the terrain west of the then young settlement of Alice Springs, and was the first white man to climb Ayers Rock, which he named after the governor of the time. We were later to follow his tracks to the Rock, and make the famed ascent. The climb is unrelentingly steep, a severe test of the friction of one's soles, not to mention one's nerve. Part way up we paused to look down, seemingly vertically, on to Maggie's Spring; it was from that point that Gosse scaled Ayers Rock, on a route surely twice as steep as the tourist trod we plied.

The Bluff named after him is something of a geological puzzle. Volcanic activity can fairly certainly be eliminated as the cause of the crater, and bubble formations also seem unlikely following drilling by oil exploration companies. An impact therefore remains the best-buy theory. But a strange impact it must have been, for the crater does not appear to have been excavated much below the surrounding terrain, yet its diameter, more than a mile, would lead one to expect a significant depression. Too, those rock strata in the walls seem to have survived remarkably well. Most puzzling, however, is the fact that the Bluff we see today is only the central portion of a ringed complex more than ten miles across. Geologists have known of the giant structure for many years, though no obvious surface features can be made out by the untrained eye. Satellite photographs show the structure well, and confirm that the Bluff lies exactly at its centre. What sort of impact will devastate a ten-mile area, but leave so crisp a one-mile crater in its centre? Not knowing how much erosion to attribute to the region since the impact, this is an unanswerable question, but one that lends itself nicely to speculation. One of the more interesting ideas is that the impacting object was a small comet. We are still unsure of the internal structure of comets, but one school of thought postulates a small rocky core surrounded by a fluff of ice. The impact of such a body might well generate a structure like Gosse's Bluff, the central core producing the crater whilst the icy crust flattens the surrounding terrain in a less dramatic way.

We left the experts to ponder the origin of Gosse's Bluff, and made our way west and south to visit the other highlights of the region. There are some dramatic places thereabouts. But when we returned to Sydney and began to look back over our slides and memories, we realised that Gosse's Bluff had truly been one of the

Figure 3. Looking into Gosse's Bluff from the east rim. The roughly circular wall curves round in the distance, whilst the foreground shadows cover the access track into the floor.

highlights of our trip.

One day somebody may buy Gosse's Bluff, and build a good road to its heart. As at that pathetic little scoop in Winslow, Arizona, they will make a fortune selling trinkets to tourists who will learn to include it in their Grand Tour of Australia. Should that day come, I will vow never to go near the place again. To journey, expedition fashion, across the vast inland of Australia, and to come upon such places as I have described here, remains a challenge and a reward that should never be denied mankind.

FIONA VINCENT

Vermin of the Sky

Minor planets, or asteroids, have generally been somewhat neglected. Indeed, professional astronomers have been known to refer to them as the 'vermin of the sky'. In astronomy books they are generally tucked in at the end of the section on the Solar System – along with such odds and ends as comets, meteors, the Zodiacal Light, and the Gegenschein. But we are discovering now that many of these objects are related. And minor planets are proving to be very interesting in their own right.

Broadly speaking, minor planets are small bodies orbiting the Sun, mostly (but not all) between the orbits of Mars and Jupiter. They therefore come at the change-over point between the inner, small rocky planets and the outer, giant gas planets – this may be significant in considering their origins. When first discovered, they were thought to be the remains of a planet that had broken up. The early seventeenth century astronomer Kepler, pointing out that there appeared to be a planet missing between Mars and Jupiter, suggested that perhaps it had been destroyed by God because of the wickedness of its inhabitants. Many science-fiction writers have developed this theme in one way or another; one popular concept is that of an advanced civilization that discovered nuclear power and succeeded in blowing itself up. Like Kepler's theory, this is obviously intended as an Awful Warning to us here on Earth! But in fact most astronomers now reckon that the minor planets are the components of a planet that, for some reason, never formed in the first place.

Current theories of the origin of the Solar System suggest that it began as a cloud of gas and dust surrounding the new Sun. Gradually it became differentiated into light and heavy components, and eddies appeared in it where the matter was concentrated. Eventually these eddies produced large numbers of small proto-planets, and these collided and stuck together to form larger bodies. The heavier elements, nearer the Sun, formed the solid planets like the Earth; the lighter elements further out formed the giant gas planets like Jupiter. Many of the ancient surfaces of the planets and their moons bear witness to the late stages of their formation; they are covered with craters where the last few lumps of interplanetary matter impacted the surface.

For some reason the protoplanets between Mars and Jupiter did not stick together beyond a certain point. This may be due to the composition of the nebula at this point, or perhaps to the very strong tidal forces imposed by Jupiter. It seems that the accretion process got as far as forming about a dozen large spherical bodies, but that collisions after that caused them to break up instead of sticking together. Today, there remain only a few of these large bodies – Ceres, Pallas and perhaps Vesta; the remainder of the minor planets are small, irregular fragments.

Discovery

Ceres is the largest of the minor planets, but it is only 1000 km across (less than one-third of the diameter of our Moon); the brightest one is not Ceres, but Vesta, which never reaches a brightness much greater than 6th magnitude (and so cannot normally be seen by the unaided eye). Thus it is not surprising that the existence of the minor planets remained unsuspected until less than 200 years ago. The cause of their eventual discovery was a bit of numerical mysticism know as 'Bode's Law' (see Table 1). The name is erroneous, because it is not a law and it was not discovered by Bode – he merely publicized it.

As the table shows, by taking the sequence of numbers 0,1,2,4,8 etc. (where each number is twice the preceding one) and juggling with it, one can obtain a sequence that corresponds fairly closely to the distances of the planets from the Sun – provided we insert a 'missing' planet at a distance of 2.8 Astronomical Units (AU). When first published by the German astronomer Bode in the mid-eighteenth century, this table could only be compared with the planetary distances as far as Saturn, and was little more than a curiosity. However, the discovery of Uranus in 1781 seemed to provide confirmation of the 'Law', since its distance of 19.2 AU tallied remarkably well. (Unfortunately, subsequent planetary discoveries have not continued this trend: Neptune, at 30.1 AU, falls into a gap between two terms in the sequence, and Pluto, at

TABLE I

Bode's Law

Sequence		0	1	2	4	8	16	32	64	128
×3		0	3	6	12	24	48	96	192	384
+4		4	7	10	16	28	52	100	196	388
/10		0.4	0.7	1.0	1.6	2.8	5.2	10.0	19.6	38.8

Planets	Mercury	Venus	Earth	Mars	?	Jupiter	Saturn
Distances	0.4	0.7	1	1.5	2.8	5.2	9.5

about 39.8 AU, occurs roughly where Neptune should be. Bode's Law is not generally given much credence nowadays, although a few astronomers have tried to produce adaptations of it, with limited success).

To provide the final confirmation of his 'Law', Bode needed to find the missing planet at 2.8 AU. He assumed it would be found, like all the other planets, near the ecliptic (the apparent path of the Sun accross the sky). He organized a meeting of other German astronomers, and divided up the ecliptic among these 'celestial police', so that they could search it for the missing planet. Some sections of the ecliptic were left for eminent astronomers in other countries; one of those was Giuseppe Piazzi, director of the observatory at Palermo in Sicily.

Piazzi apparently did not know of this: he was fully occupied in compiling a new star-catalogue. Astronomy, then and now, depends ultimately on good star-catalogues. For example, you can only measure the position of a new object by comparing it with stars whose positions are already known and catalogued; the accuracy of your results depend on the accuracy of your catalogue. Catalogues in Piazzi's day varied in accuracy, and there were some discrepancies between them: Piazzi was in the process of compiling a new catalogue that would combine the best of the existing ones with his own careful observations. On the evening of January 1, 1801, he was trying to fix the position of a star which was causing him some problems, when he realized that he had discovered a moving 'star' – presumably a comet, he thought, though it showed no signs of fuzziness. He sent word to other European astronomers, and continued to observe it himself.

Unfortunately, Piazzi fell ill six weeks later, and communications were so slow in those days that no-one was able to carry on his observations before the planet had disappeared into the daylight sky.

According to the state of mathematics at the time, the new object should now have been irrevocably lost, having been observed over an arc of only 3 degrees – insufficient to calculate its orbit. However, a young maths tutor called Karl Freidrich Gauss (a name now all too familiar to anyone who has studied almost any branch of mathematics or physics!) seized upon this opportunity. He had been working in his spare time on a way of fitting a curve of any desired shape to a set of observations. Piazzi's observations were published, in the first international scientific periodical, 'Monatliche Korrespondenz'. Gauss succeeded in finding a planet-ary-type orbit that would fit them; he then predicted where the planet should reappear after conjunction with the Sun. On December 31, 1801, another of the German astronomers, Olbers, found the new planet, just where Gauss had predicted. The foundations of Gauss' fame as a mathematician were laid; Piazzi, as original discoverer of the planet, was invited to name it, and called it 'Ceres' after the patron goddess of Sicily.

Unfortunately, the newly discovered 'missing planet', though at the right distance from the Sun, was disappointingly small. Herschel, the discoverer of Uranus, would hardly admit it to be a planet at all. He pointed out that it showed no disk in the telescope, but appeared star-like – 'asteroidal'; the name 'asteroid' for this class of objects has regrettably stuck. Perhaps no-one was greatly surprised when Olbers, still methodically searching his allotted section of the ecliptic, discovered a second planet in 1802; it was named Pallas. Juno and Vesta followed in 1804 and 1807; and there matters stood for many years. The fifth minor planet, Astræa, was not discovered till both Bode and Piazzi were dead, in 1845. However, with the arrival of astronomical photography, hundreds more were found, appearing on photographs as short lines or as dots masquerading as stars – hence the name of 'vermin'.

Nowadays over 3000 minor planets are known, in the sense that their orbits have been determined; this requires a minimum of three observations. There must be many more that have been observed only once or twice. The positions of the known ones are published yearly in the Leningrad 'Ephemerides of Minor Planets'. The most recent discoveries appear only with numbers to identify them, but most of them also have proper names. Naturally, the supply of minor gods and goddesses ran out at an early stage. Many have been named after places on Earth, where, presumably, they were discovered – like (232)Russia, (241)Germania, (439)Ohio, (334)Chicago; some appear to have been named after the discoverers' wives or girl-friends – (291)Alice, (517)Edith, or (1486)Marilyn. Many commemorate celebrated astronomers; number 1000, for example, was named Piazzia. Nowadays, the authorities do not insist on adding '–a' to a name, nor does the astronomer in question need to be dead; recently named planets include (2602)Moore and (2709)Sagan. Another minor planet has recently been named (2830)Greenwich, to commemorate the centenary of the Greenwich Meridian.

Orbits

The first minor planet, Ceres, was, as expected, at a distance of almost exactly 2.8 AU from the Sun, but this does not apply to all of them by any means, as Figure 1 shows. It is helpful to look, not only at the distance of a minor planet from the Sun, but also at its average speed as it goes round its orbit. By Kepler's third law, these are related, since the cube of the average speed varies inversely as the square of the distance from the Sun – the diagram shows both. Most of them lie between 2.2 and 3.2 AU, but there are many outside this range, and the distribution is very uneven. Why are there distinct gaps, for example at 2.5 AU (900″/day) and 2.8 AU (750″/day)? And why are there large peaks like the one at 3.15 AU (630″/day)? These problems have occupied astronomers and mathematicians for many years; the gaps are named 'Kirkwood gaps', after the researcher who first drew attention to them.

It is worth pointing out, first, that classical mathematics cannot give a complete answer to this sort of problem. If the problem were simply one of a single planet or asteroid orbiting the Sun – 'two-body problem' – then it could be solved exactly, as Kepler showed; if you know the position and velocity of the planet at any instant, you can work out its path for any length of time before or after. But if there are two planets orbiting the Sun – 'three-body problem' – then the orbit of each planet is affected by the other, and classical mathematics simply cannot cope. Obviously the case of the Solar System with its numerous planets – known as 'n-body problem' – is even worse! You can get approximate solutions which are valid for a certain length of time – they are used for the

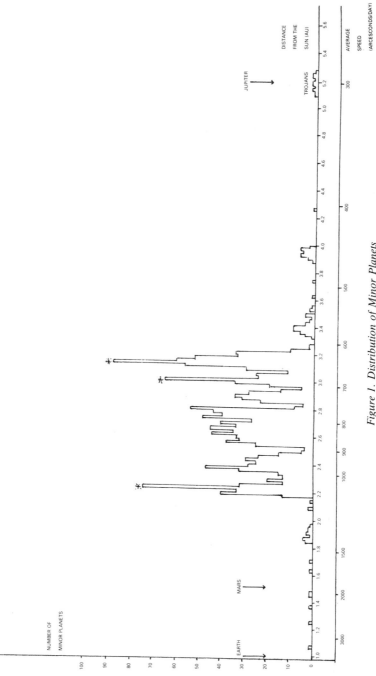

Figure 1. Distribution of Minor Planets
(*marks families with related orbits)

predictions in this *Yearbook,* for example. But no exact long-term solution can be found.

The orbit of a minor planet is therefore changing all the time. However, it is possible to find certain parameters of the orbit which stay constant. If a group of minor planets all have the same values for these parameters, then it suggests that they once shared the same orbit: in fact, that they are fragments of what was once a single body. These 'families' are part of the reason for the uneven distribution; they probably explain the peak at 3.15 AU, and the other two marked peaks. The rest of the unevenness is largely due to the effect of Jupiter.

One group of minor planets, known as the Trojans, is a very good example. These appear in the figure as a small group around 5.2 AU – in other words, they are at the same distance from the Sun as Jupiter. However, they are not in the same place as Jupiter is – some are 60 degrees ahead of the planet, and the rest are 60 degrees behind it. In either case, the Sun, Jupiter, and the minor planet always form an equilateral triangle, and classical mathematics can prove that this special configuration is in fact stable over a long period of time. The first few minor planets discovered in this situation had been named after heroes of the Trojan War, so all subsequent discoveries in these groups have been given similar names. It would have been logical to place the Greek heroes together in one group, and the Trojans in the other, but in fact they are all mixed up together.

A lot of the other peaks and gaps in the minor planet distribution can be explained in terms of a phenomenon called 'resonance'.

Consider a planet like Ceres, which is at 2.8 AU from the Sun. Its average speed is about 770″/day, which bears no simple relation to Jupiter's speed of 300″/day. Over a long enough period of time, Jupiter and Ceres will take up just about every possible configuration. This means that Jupiter will pull Ceres in every possible direction, and so the perturbing effect of Jupiter on Ceres' orbit will eventually 'average out'.

But now consider a minor planet at a distance of about 2.5 AU from the Sun, with an average speed of 900″/day. This one moves exactly three times as fast as Jupiter, so at every third orbit the minor planet 'sees' Jupiter in the same place. The same few configurations of Jupiter and the minor planet keep occurring over and over again. This means that the forces that Jupiter exerts on this minor planet tend to build up over a long period of time. The two bodies are said to be 'in resonance with' each other.

It is often asserted that a planet like this, whose speed bears a simple relation to Jupiter's speed, should be in an unstable orbit: wait long enough, and the accumulated forces from Jupiter should move it into a different orbit. And it is true that there are very few minor planets with average speeds of 750″/day and 900″/day (2 and 2.5 times Jupiter's). On the other hand, there is actually a small cluster with an average speed of around 450″/day (1.5 times Jupiter's), so the situation is not that simple. This problem is not confined to the minor planets; most of the major planets have average speeds that are in resonance with one another, and yet the orbits of the major planets appear to be stable! There are probably similar mechanisms going on in the case of Saturn's rings, where the tiny ice-particles cluster in narrow rings with gaps in between, due to the perturbing effects of Saturn's moons. We are a long way from a complete understanding of resonance phenomena.

In any case, not all the minor planets are confined to the main belt between Mars and Jupiter. A few, like (944)Hidalgo (not shown in the diagram), travel outside Jupiter's orbit part of the time. Recently, a small body was discovered which looks like an asteroid, but orbits at 13.6 AU from the Sun, outside the orbit of Saturn! Whether this is the first-discovered of a whole new group of minor planets between Jupiter and Saturn, or whether it is an isolated body, can not yet be determined for certain – it has been named as a minor planet, (2060)Chiron. We know that the moons of Mars, and the outer moons of Jupiter, are small and irregular, and are probably captured asteroids; perhaps the small moons of Saturn were similarly captured from an outer asteroid belt.

There are also a number of asteroids which orbit closer to the Sun than does Mars; some even come closer than the Earth, and so cross the Earth's orbit. One very recent discovery, known so far only as 1984 QA, has almost the same orbit as the Earth – it is at a distance of 0.989 AU from the Sun, and takes just 359 days to go round the Sun. There is a theory that some of these 'Earth-crossing' minor planets are actually the remains of short-period comets. Since a comet loses some of its gas and dust every time it passes the Sun, it seems likely that eventually it may be stripped down to a bare rocky core. Many comets have left a stream of particles, which we observe each year as a meteor shower, though we cannot always find which comet caused a particular shower.

One minor planet has recently been discovered which has a very similar orbit to the particles in the Geminid meteor shower. No comet has ever been found to link with the Geminids, but now it seems as though the newly discovered asteroid may be all that remains of the parent comet.

Meteor-showers are generally composed of tiny particles which burn up high in the Earth's atmosphere. The occasional much larger bodies which fall all the way to the Earth's surface, to be found as meteorites, are not usually connected with meteor showers. In only a few cases has the orbit of a meteorite been calculated, and in each case it resembles the orbit of an Earth-crossing asteroid. So there appears to be a link between most of the odds and ends of the Solar System – comets, meteors, meteorites and asteroids. Even the Zodiacal Light and the Gegenschein are tied in, because they are due to a ring of dust lying in the plane of the Solar System, reflecting the sunlight very faintly. The Infra-Red Satellite, IRAS, discovered large quantities of dust in the asteroid belt, presumably the remains of fragmented minor planets.

Observing Minor Planets

Until recently, analysing the orbits of the minor planets was virtually the only way of studying them. This was – and is – carried out photographically. A photograph is obtained of a part of the sky including the minor planet; if it is a long exposure, the minor planet will show up as a short line, because it has moved during the time the photograph was being taken, but this makes it hard to measure its position accurately. It is better to take as short an exposure as possible, and get a small star-like image; the problem then is to find which 'star' is the minor planet! The usual way is to take two photographs at different times, and compare them in some device such as a blink microscope. One 'star' will have moved – that is the minor planet. The position of the minor planet image on the photograph is measured, together with the positions of some of the genuine stars which also appear in the picture.

The positions of these stars are looked up in a star catalogue (the sort of catalogue Piazzi produced). Some number-crunching then gives the position of the minor planet in the sky: this is often done using a technique based on one that Gauss invented. Three such positions at different times (ideally, with a fortnight's gap between them) are needed to calculate an elliptical orbit for the minor planet: again, Gauss devised one of the ways of doing this. In fact, the orbit of the minor planet is constantly being perturbed by Jupiter and the other major planets, so the calculated orbit is only valid for a short time; the technical term for it is the 'osculating' orbit, which is the same as the planet's true path only for a short time. ('Osculating' literally means 'kissing').

Nowadays, minor planets can be studied in many ways other than merely measuring their positions. For example, if a minor planet has an irregular shape and is spinning, there will be tiny variations in the amount of sunlight it reflects. A photometer attached to a telescope can measure this effect. Alternatively, photometers can be used to measure the brightness of a minor planet both at visual wavelengths and in infrared, and from these astronomers can deduce something of the nature of the planet's surface. Few minor planets are bright enough for the light to be split up into a full spectrum for analysis, but in many cases the amount of light can be measured at several different colours, giving the same sort of information.

In these ways, several different classes of minor planet can now be distinguished – different in colour and brightness, and presumably also in composition. There are bright asteroids like Vesta, which resemble the type of meteorites known as achondrites; they are made of a rock like basalt, which has been altered by volcanic processes. The majority of the minor planets, though, are much darker, and resemble the carbonaceous chondrite meteorites; some have a reddish colour. Others are reddish but bright, and may be a mixture of silicates and iron; they do not resemble any known class of meteorites. And there are a few metallic asteroids, largely composed of iron and nickel, which resemble metallic meteorites, like the famous Arizona one. There is a change in composition of asteroids in different parts of the main asteroid belt; carbonaceous and silicate planets are both found near the inner edge, but at the outer edge only the dark carbonaceous ones occur.

But there is still much more we should like to know about minor planets. If our theories of the origin of the Solar System are correct, then the minor planets are very little different from the original proto-planets. Where full-size planets formed, about 4600 million years ago, the material in the proto-planets was subjected to all sorts of processes: the rock was deformed by the greater gravity, changed by heat due to radioactivity, and so forth – all the processes that we call 'geology'. None of the rocks we can find on the Earth is older than about 3800 million years. But the rocks in the asteroid belt should be virtually unchanged from the birth of the Solar System. The minor planets could also be of use to us. The low gravity on a minor planet means that a space-ship could land and take off again, with a cargo, without expending much energy. Minerals from the surface of the minor planet could be brought back to Earth relatively easily, and might supplement the dwindling natural resources of this planet. Perhaps, in the more distant future, it might be possible to divert a minor planet into an orbit close to the Earth, for our own convenience. This is science-fiction at the moment, but does not require technology very much advanced on what we have now.

Certainly plans are afoot to send space-probes to the minor planets. After 1989, all the major planets except Pluto will have been visited by space-probe, so it is high time to turn to the minor planets. There are plans for the Jupiter probe Galileo to study one or two minor planets on its way to the giant planet, and this will undoubtedly add greatly to our knowledge, but a high-speed fly-by can produce only a limited amount of data. However, it may not be necessary to build a special satellite to visit the asteroids; a modified weather satellite designed to orbit the Earth could easily do the job. It could fly past several minor planets, or go into orbit round one particular one. Eventually it might be decided to crash-land the satellite on the surface of an asteroid. The crash will be made as gentle as possible, but we can't expect a genuine soft-landing – we don't even know yet what sort of surface we are trying to land on!

This high-technology approach to the minor planets should not hide the fact that it is a very useful field for amateur astronomers. Perhaps the single most important way in which amateurs can advance minor planet astronomy is in the field of occultations. When a minor planet passes in front of a star, it blocks out the starlight, because the shadow of the minor planet crosses part of the Earth. If observers over a wide area note carefully the times of disappearance and reappearance of the star, these observations can all be combined to give the overall shape of the shadow – and consequently the shape of the minor planet. This was carried out recently in the USA with Pallas, and almost the entire outline of the asteroid was mapped. There is also the intriguing possibility that some of the minor planets may have satellites, or occur in pairs; occultation observations may confirm this. Predictions of minor planet occultations are published each year, in this *Yearbook* and in other places; it is well worth while taking part in such an exercise.

It is possible to observe minor planets in between occultations, of course! Binoculars will easily pick out some of the larger ones. Some amateurs have telescopes with photometers, and can measure the fluctuations in brightness of minor planets as they rotate. Measuring positions on photographs is also well within the capabilities of many amateurs. It is by no means impossible to discover a new minor planet; any photograph showing stars down to 15th or 16th magnitude should be inspected for trails. The trailed image should be measured, and its position will show whether or not it is one of the known minor planets.

The British Astronomical Association has recently formed a Minor Planets Section, which will be able to help to identify such an object. The Section will be happy to give all sorts of help and advice on observing these fascinating little objects, which still hold so many mysteries.

JOHN DAVIES

1983TB and the Geminids

In addition to heralding the onset of the festive season the second
and third weeks in December mark the annual appearance of the
Geminid meteor shower. The Geminids, which reach a peak on
December 13 or 14, are one of the most reliable and prolific
meteor showers, although observations from Europe are often
hampered by the coming of winter and its attendant cloudy nights.
That the Geminids is a rich shower, and worth braving the
customary low temperatures to observe, can be seen by comparing
its average Zenithal Hourly Rate (ZHR) of about 60 to that of
other well-known showers such as the Perseids (40) and the
Leonids (6). Of course the ZHR is a rather artificial number,
being the number of meteors seen per hour by a keen-eyed
observer at a dark observing site with a totally unobstructed
horizon on a clear, moonless night with the meteors coming from
directly overhead, but it is useful for comparing the properties of
various streams under different conditions. The Geminids are,
however, more than a reliable celestial firework display; they raise
several important questions regarding the connection between
meteors, comets and certain types of rather unusual asteroids.
Before looking at the details of the Geminid shower, it would be
helpful to examine the general properties of meteors, or shooting
stars as they are more popularly known. A meteor is the brief flash
of light which streaks across the night sky marking the final
seconds of a tiny piece of interplanetary dust burning up in the
atmosphere. Most of these dust particles, usually referred to as
meteoroids, have masses as low as one millionth of a gram, but
since they are arriving at higher relative speeds of about 36,000
miles an hour they have enough energy to produce a brief trail of
incandescent atoms in the upper air.
Since interplanetary space contains many of these dust particles,

the Earth regularly sweeps them up in its yearly voyage around the Sun and several meteors may be seen each hour by simply gazing at a dark, night sky. Actually the hourly rate varies throughout the night, increasing in the pre-dawn hours as the Earth's rotation brings the observer to the leading side of the planet where the higher relative speed means that more meteors become bright enough to be seen by the naked eye, so the early morning is preferred by dedicated meteor observers.

Most nights the meteors seem to come equally from all directions and they are said to be sporadic, but at certain times of the year the meteors seem to show a distinct preference for a certain region of the sky. In such circumstances the meteors are said to be members of a shower. If the tracks of meteors in a shower are plotted on a star chart they appear to be coming from a small region of sky called the radiant. Each shower is named after the constellation in which the radiant lies, so the Geminids appear to be coming from the direction of the heavenly twins. Interestingly, one shower is named after a constellation that no longer exists. Quadrans Muralis, the constellation of the mural quadrant, was introduced in 1795 by the French astronomer Joseph de Lalande but quickly fell into disuse. However, it did survive long enough to give its name to the Quadrantid meteors. The stars of Quadrans were eventually returned to their original homes in Boötes and Hercules, but the meteors have retained their delightfully anacronistic name.

Meteor showers come about because in addition to the general interplanetary dust there are specific streams of meteoroids which orbit the Sun, and when the Earth intercepts such a stream a meteor shower is produced. Since the orbits of the Earth and stream change only slowly, the point of intersection remains virtually constant from year to year and the shower always appears from the same radiant.

The origin of these dust streams was realized in the 1860s when Kirkwood suggested that they were connected with comets and this was confirmed when Schiaparelli showed that the Perseid shower, which occurs in August, shared the orbit of comet Swift–Tuttle (1862 III).

Gradually more meteor showers were linked to specific comets, possibly the most famous being that of Biela's comet, which broke up in the mid-nineteenth century to produce the Andromedid meteor shower. The Andromedid meteors were clearly the remains of Biela's comet, although the shower has by now almost completely faded away.

The link between Biela's comet and the Andromedids confirmed the connection between comets and meteors, but a full understanding of the relationship was only reached when the dirty snowball model of comets was developed. In the 1950's Fred Whipple proposed that comets were in fact kilometre-sized snowballs orbiting the Sun. As the snowball, more properly called the nucleus, is warmed by the Sun the ice sublimes and gas and dust is released to form the fuzzy coma and tail which characterizes comets. The dust is blown away from the nucleus by the gas pressure, giving it a small relative velocity and so it does not follow the comet's orbit precisely. Dust emitted from the sunward side of the comet will move into an orbit of slightly shorter period and so will move ahead of the nucleus, whereas dust released from the opposite face will gradually be left behind. Eventually some of the dust drifting ahead of the comet will meet up with the dust trailing behind and a complete loop of meteoroids will be formed. We can thus determine the approximate age of the shower by examining how it behaves from year to year.

The meteoroids in a young shower will not have had time to spread right around the orbit, so in some years the display will be more dramatic than others, depending on whether the Earth happens to intercept one of the denser regions of meteoroids. On the other hand, if the number of meteors seen is fairly constant each year, this means that the dust is well spread around the orbit, implying that the shower is older. As the shower ages still more, the meteoroids will spread further apart and so the duration of the shower will increase because of the longer time it takes for the Earth to travel across the width of the stream. This gradual widening of the stream will also make the location of the shower radiant harder to determine precisely, since it will appear to cover a larger region of the sky. The Geminids, with a shower duration of about nine days, seem to be fairly old, although the precise age of the shower is hard to determine since the stream width also depends on the size of the original comet, and this is not known for the Geminids – but more of this later.

The Geminids were apparently not known in antiquity, although a few ancient fireball records from the eleventh century have been linked with the shower, and Geminid meteors were first reported regularly in the nineteenth century. The first reliable reports of the radiant were made in 1862 by the British astronomer Greg and also the same year by Marsh and Twinning in the USA. The shower was further studied by members of the British Astronomical Association around the turn of the century, when the position of the radiant was defined more precisely.

From these observations, and similar ones made by other meteor astronomers, it was possible to calculate the orbit of the Geminid stream, and this turned out to be unusual in two respects. Firstly, the orbit has a very short period, only about one and a half years, and secondly no parent comet could be found. The orbit derived for the Geminid shower did, however, explain why the shower was not reported before the nineteenth century, since calculations showed that the dust stream is affected by Jupiter's gravity and probably only began to intercept the Earth's orbit about one or two hundred years ago. This same effect means that the Geminids will only be visible from Earth for a short time, since the orbit will continue to evolve and by about the begining of the twenty-second century the paths of Earth and the meteoroids will no longer cross.

With the orbit of the shower established, and no parent comet to observe, astronomers concentrated their studies of the shower on determining how much material was actually found in the meteor stream and how it was distributed. Amongst these astronomers was Dr David Hughes of Sheffield University, who has deduced that the stream contains about 9,000,000 tons of dust, contained in a doughnut-shaped cloud about 13,000,000 kilometres in cross section. The meteoroids are travelling at an average speed of 34.2 kilometres per second relative to the Earth and each year about 15 tons of meteoritic material is deposited in the upper atmosphere during the shower. Surprisingly, although the Geminids deposit much more meteoritic dust than the other well-known showers (about 5 tons per year come from the Perseids and Quadrantids combined) the influx of dust from showers is still small compared to the daily arrival of 44 tons per day in the form of sporadic meteors. Hughes, with Ken Fox and Iwan Williams of Queen Mary College, also developed computer simulations of how the shower was formed by the slow disintegration of a comet which they believed to have completely disappeared by now and hence has never been found.

This was the situation when on October 11 1983 Simon Green and I, both then working at Leicester University, discovered a new fast-moving object in data returned from the Infrared Astronomical Satellite IRAS. The positions of the new object were telexed to Mount Palomar where by good fortune Charles Kowal, a well-known asteroid observer, was observing with the 48-inch Schmidt telescope. Kowal's photographs confirmed the IRAS discovery and showed that the object was a 15th magnitude asteroid. From the positions reported by IRAS, and by Kowal and other astronomers over the next few days, a preliminary orbit for the new asteroid was calculated and it was given the temporary designation 1983TB by the International Astronomical Union. (The designation simply indicates that it was the second asteroid reported in the first half of October 1983).

The orbit of 1983TB was announced in an IAU telegram which showed it to be a member of the Apollo family, a group of kilometre-sized asteroids whose orbits cross that of the Earth. The orbital calculations also showed that 1983TB was a rather special Apollo, since it approached the Sun more closely than any other known asteroid. At perihelion 1983TB is only 20,000,000 kilometres from the Sun's surface, about 6,000,000 kilometres closer than the previous record holder, asteroid 1566 Icarus.

Even more exciting news was soon to come, because when additional photographs had been taken and the orbital parameters of 1983TB had been improved, it was realized that the orbit of the new asteroid was almost the same as that of the Geminid meteor shower. This news immediately raised the possibility that 1983TB was not a normal asteroid but the long sought-after Geminid parent body, and sent several asteroid astronomers rushing back to their telescopes to search for evidence of a cometary coma around 1983TB. Unfortunately at the time of discovery 1983TB had already made its closest approach to Earth and was fading rapidly as it receded back into space. A one-hour exposure photograph made about a week after the discovery showed no evidence of cometary activity, but there was no time for detailed follow up observations before 1983TB faded from view. This left the true nature of the object ambiguous, the association with the Geminids and the small perihelion distance point to a very faint comet while its appearance in ground-based photographs and its aphelion (farthest point from the Sun) in the main asteroid belt imply that it is a normal Apollo asteroid. The truth, however, may lie in between; 1983TB may be a transition object, a comet in the process of becoming an asteroid.

The possibility of an evolutionary link between comets and Apollo asteroids is not new, it was put forwards by Öpik when he tried to explain the population of Apollo objects. Öpik, and others, reasoned that since the Apollos cross the Earth's orbit then occasional collisions must occur, and this process will gradually remove them all. Calculations showed that unless the Apollos were steadily topped up they would all have disappeared long ago and since they have clearly not all vanished astronomers began to work for a means of replacing those lost by collision.

One possibility considered was that the Apollo objects might be small asteroids ejected from the main asteroid belt into Earth-crossing orbits. However, since the two types of orbit are quite different, it was not easy to see how this change could be accomplished; for example, a collision between two asteroids is more likely to shatter them completely than to eject one intact into an Earth-crossing orbit. The other transfer mechanism involves subtle gravitational interactions between main belt asteroids and the planets, notably Jupiter. It is well known that Jupiter's gravity affects the asteroids, sweeping certain parts of the main belt almost completely clear and leaving the so-called Kirkwood gaps. It may be possible for an asteroid on the edge of one of the Kirkwood gaps to be ejected into an Apollo-type orbit under special circumstances, but the precise details of this process are not yet well understood.

The theoretical difficulties of explaining the Apollos as escaped main belt asteroids led to the proposal that the source of the new Apollos was from the decay of short-period comets. This theory follows naturally from the Whipple's dirty snowball model of a cometary nucleus. Each time a comet goes around the Sun, some of its outer layers are boiled away to form the coma and tail and recent estimates suggest that the comet loses about the top one metre or so of its crust each orbit. However, the comet's nucleus does have a weak gravitation field and although this is unable to stop any newly released gas molecules from being blown away it is able to retain some of the dust, which eventually falls back onto the nucleus. Gradually, over many years, this process causes a build up of dust on the surface of the nucleus and this forms an insulating layer, protecting the frozen gases underneath from the heat of the Sun and reducing comentary activity. The final result of this process might well be an object about a kilometre across in an

Earth-approaching orbit which would be indistinguishable from an asteroid without very close inspection.

Estimates of the rate of cometary decay required to sustain the Apollo population suggest that the theory is plausible, but a major drawback has always been that while plenty of asteroids and comets are known, no transition objects have been found. This was regarded by many as a fatal flaw in the theory, but one which may have been removed by the discovery of 1983TB.

The key position that 1983TB holds in the proposed evolutionary path from comet to asteroid means that important observations are needed to define unambiguously the nature of the object. One crucial test is to search for any evidence of a faint coma around 1983TB. Since no coma was seen in visible light at the time of discovery, an alternative might be to search in infrared wavelengths. Infrared observations may be helpful since any dust in the vicinity of 1983TB will radiate most of its energy at these wavelengths. If the infrared measurements reveal that there is a cloud of dust around 1983TB it would certainly point to its being a very faint comet. Other types of observation are also possible; for example, it is possible to search for features typical of specific minerals in the infrared spectrum of the object. Asteroids are known to have absorption features in their infrared spectra which can be related by laboratory measurements to specific minerals, and these features are not seen in comets, although comets have their own characteristic spectra. Comparisons of the visible spectra of comets and typical asteroids to that of 1983TB are also crucial in resolving the true nature of the new object. Fortunately, 1983TB made another comparitively close approach to the Earth in 1984 and in early September the object was recovered by Jim Gibson using the 48-inch Schmidt telescope at Mount Palomar. 1983TB made its closest approach to Earth in December, and was under study from various observatories throughout the year. The full details of these observations are not yet available, but first results do not seem to support the dead comet hypothesis.

None of the astronomers who observed 1983TB reported any evidence for a cometary coma, and the visual magnitude was about what was expected for a normal asteroid. First reports of the spectrum also seem more consistent with an asteroidal surface, although the infrared spectrum appears to be quite unusual for an Apollo object. Observations reported from the Kitt Peak National Observatory indicate that no cometary features were seen in the visible spectrum of 1983TB, and significantly that its colour is typical of the S, or stony, type of asteroid rather than the C (carbonaceous) type which might have been expected for an extinct comet nucleus.

It may be that further analysis of these observations will shed more light on the mystery of 1983TB. This is necessary because one important question still remains; if 1983TB is not a dead comet, then what is the origin of the Geminid meteors?

Analysis of infrared observations made at the UK Infrared Telescope in Hawaii during December 1984 suggest that 1983TB, now designated Minor Planet number 3200, has a rocky surface and is rotating rapidly. Both these results cast further doubt on the suggestion that the object is an extinct cometary nucleus.

Editor's Note.

The name 'Phæthon' has been proposed for 1983TB, but has yet to be officially ratified.

ERIC H. STRACH

Observing the Sun in Hydrogen Alpha

Recent years have seen great strides in the development of solar astronomy. Sophisticated equipment is being used to study the Sun both by earth-bound professional observatories and from space vehicles such as the Solar Maximum Mission and the Orbiting Solar Observatory.

In the light of these highly technical developments the amateur astronomer must feel humble and ask himself what there is left for him to do in the field of solar work with his modest equipment. In the following pages I will try to show that there are still fields that can be usefully explored by the keen amateur and that this work can be most interesting and rewarding and may in a small way contribute some useful information.

The Sun, being the nearest star, is the only star which lends itself to more detailed study – it is the only star whose surface can be seen in detail, although in the not too distant future the surface of other stars and possibly their surrounding planets may be seen with the planned, multiple array space-telescope.

Study of the Sun in white light is interesting; the ever changing appearance of the photosphere, its cyclical behaviour, the development, life, and fate of sunspots provide rewarding work. Under good seeing conditions detailed study of faculæ, particularly of polar faculæ, during sunspot minimum, of solar granulations, and pore formation can be done and may fill some gaps in our knowledge. White light work of the Sun can be extended and complemented by choosing one or another part of the electro-magnetic emission of energy by the Sun for further study, be it radio waves or special lines of the visible spectrum. I recommend solar observation in Hydrogen alpha [Hα] light since Hydrogen is the predominant element in the Sun. Hα studies have greatly extended and enhanced interest in solar work. But right from the onset it must be emphasized that white-light observation still remains the basic study and any more specialized work must be related to it.

All early work was done spectroscopically. Janssen and Lockyer in 1868 were the first to observe prominences outside an eclipse using a spectroscope: the slit centred on the Hα line is trained tangentially around the solar limb and prominences can be seen in the emission line of hydrogen.

George Ellery Hale invented and constructed the spectroheliograph in 1892 which has since undergone several modifications. A vibrating slit scans an area of the solar disk so that prominences and disk features can be visualized. It is an instrument for professional astronomers, although a few dedicated and skilled amateurs have successfully constructed and used it.

With the advent of the birefringent filter the study of the chromosphere and prominences has been greatly simplified and brought well within the reach of the amateur solar observer.

The French astronomer Bernard Lyot developed this monochromatic filter in 1933. Briefly, light is passed through a polaroid making it vibrate in one direction; next, it passes through a quartz plate (or Icelandic spar), as a result of which double refraction occurs: one beam vibrating parallel to the quartz crystal axis, the other at 90°. Next, the light passes through a further polaroid which brings the beam back to the same plane but a phase difference has occurred: some colours are removed by interference, others are reinforced. Further passages through increasing thicknesses of quartz plates and through further polaroids reduce the number of bands until they are sufficiently separated to be isolated by a red glass which allows light to pass through at the Hα line to the exclusion of all other bands. The filter action is temperature dependent: any variation of the temperature affects the thickness of the plates and therefore the refractive index and phase difference. The narrower the pass band the more sensitive the filter becomes to temperature changes. Slight changes result in a shift of the transmission band either to the blue or to the red side of the Hα line and this can be used to determine line-of-sight velocity of an eruption (Doppler shift effect). A similar effect can be obtained by tilting the filter.

A filter of a pass band of 2 to 5 Ångströms is used for observation of prominences. Not being very temperature dependent at this bandwidth it needs heating only in sub-zero conditions. It is very reasonably priced – it costs no more than a modest SLR camera. But its use has enlarged the scope of the solar observer and has raised the interest and usefulness of solar work beyond all expectations.

Horace Dall has described in detail the construction of the PROMSCOPE using a 4 Ångström Hα filter (Dall, H. E., 'Filter Type Prominence Telescope for Amateurs', *J.Brit.Astr.Ass.*, 77(2)94(1967)). The principle of the instrument is to create an artificial eclipse by placing a cone stop of suitable size in the focal plane, thus cutting out the glare of the solar surface but allowing the chromosphere and the prominences to be seen around the circumference of the cone stop through the filter. Any reader interested in constructing such an instrument should consult Dall's excellent paper. As far as I know I was the first amateur to construct the promscope after the publication of Dall's article; in spite of only rudimentary knowledge and facilities I succeeded. The joy and amazement at the first sight of prominences seen through the self constructed scope defies description!

I have studied prominences over the past ten years and I found that my daily white-light observations were supplemented and greatly enriched by this study. Certain types of prominences occur in association with a sunspot group near the solar limb, whilst other types of prominences occur independent of spot formation. Positional work made the study of prominences even more interesting. A simple graticule surrounding the image of the Sun is a useful addition to the instrument, enabling the observer to determine the latitude of the individual prominence.

In his classical spectroscopic work on prominences Father Angelo Secchi introduced the terms of 'quiescent' and 'eruptive' prominences. Quiescent prominences develop slowly and remain stable, showing very little change and may last for several solar rotations. Eruptive prominences evolve very quickly, change their configuration constantly and vanish as quickly.

Subsequent observers proposed more complicated classifications according to the origin of the prominences, their positions and their shapes.

Origin

It was thought that prominences arise in the chromosphere but more recent work suggests that the majority arise in the corona. They lie above the chromosphere but have connections with it.

Position

The position of prominences is characteristic. It has been estimated that at least one third of all prominences are associated with sunspots. Quite naturally this proportion of prominences follows the distribution in sunspot zones and their frequency will follow the sunspot cycle. Some of them may be very active and tend to erupt. The remaining proportion of prominences are not restricted to sunspot zones and are predominantly quiescent. They often occur in higher latitudes, particularly two to three years after solar maximum.

Shapes

Various shapes of prominences can be described and often the description depends on the observer's imagination. They may resemble mounds, trees or hedgerows (Figure 1). They can form arches, loops (Figure 2) or spicules. They can hover above the chromosphere like clouds and may remain suspended for several days. Loops are almost always associated with active sunspot groups and they constantly change their configuration. Like eruptive prominences they can only be recorded by serial drawings or, ideally, by cinematography or serial photographs.

Eruptive prominences show characteristically very bright condensations within their structure giving rise to an intensely red appearance which in time gives rise to eruptive streamers. Such condensations also occur as bright knots in the jets. The eruptions can reach considerable heights, which can be measured by the drift method: a stopwatch is used to measure the time taken for a feature to drift across a haircross or the edge of the field of view and the interval is easily converted into seconds of arc and to kilometres. An eruption can reach heights of hundreds of thousands of kilometres and if serial measurements are taken at given time intervals, the speed of eruption of individual ejecta can be calculated.

Eruptive prominences can be associated with limb flares and may take the shape of a geyser-like formation (Figure 3).

Quite frequently one can observe two tree-like prominences, the top of which are connected by ever changing thin jets, like electric arcs (Figure 4). This surely portrays that the pattern is determined by strong magnetic fields, the two projections being of opposite polarity.

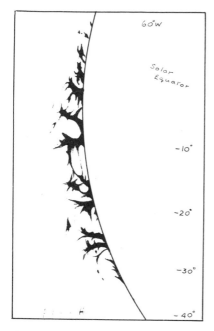

Figure 1. 'Hedgerow'-type prominences 1979 August 4 1015–1035 U.T. (Limb longitude 208°, B₀=+5°99). Drawing by Harold Hill.

Figure 2. Loop prominences on the west limb, associated with a sunspot group, the follower of which can still be seen on the disk. Note the knot-like condensations in the jets, indicating line-of-sight motion. 1982 November 26 1120 U.T.

The narrow band filter

In the last few years, the narrow band version of the birefringent interference filter has become available to the more serious amateur solar observer and has opened up new vistas for his work by enabling him to study the face of the Sun in Hα. In the past, such work was undertaken with the help of the rather elaborate set up of the spectrohelioscope. The narrow band filter with its oven has a diameter of 7.5 cm and a length of 6 cm and contains in its main's lead a small temperature control knob.

It is thus easily portable and manageable by the amateur. The filter gives a full view of the solar disk whilst the spectrohelioscope slit scans a limited area and the appearance of the solar disk has to be built up. The great advantage of the spectrohelioscope is its

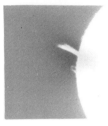

Figure 3. Photograph of a geyser-like prominence eruption which was preceded by a limb flare. 1982 July 21 1850 U.T., ¹/₂ sec exposure at prime focus on Kodak 2415.

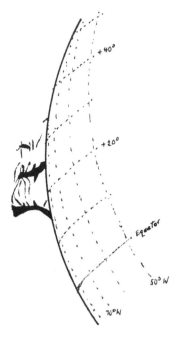

Figure 4. Interactive prominences. Two tree-like prominences connected by thin jets, resembling electric arcs. 1983 Feb.9 1205 U.T.

flexibility: it can be tuned to other spectral lines of the visible spectrum whilst the filter is made only for one wavelength, be it the hydrogen α or β or the K line of calcium. At a band width of 0.6 to 0.9 Ångström the filter shows prominences as well as disk features.

I use it in conjunction with a 203-mm Schmidt–Cassegrain telescope. Its f/ratio has to be reduced from f/10 to f/30 in order to protect the filter. This is done by suitable reduction of the aperture which is off centre in order to avoid the central obstruction of the secondary mirror. In addition the maker of the filter strongly recommends the use of an 'energy rejection filter' in the reduced aperture which eliminates the ultraviolet rays and most of the infrared radiation.

The narrow band filter has widened the field of solar work for the amateur even further and the following features have availed themselves for study.

The Chromosphere

The Sun appears as an orange-coloured disk, the surface of which shows coarse structure, the chromospheric network (Figure 5). Sunspots, which are so outstanding in white light, are also visible in the narrow band filter but are much less conspicuous; smaller spots are often difficult to see through lack of contrast against the background of the chromospheric network. At times of good seeing the fine detail of the chromospheric structure show up as a multitude of interlacing fibrils which tend to arrange themselves radially around active sunspot areas. Some fibrils form strands of longer winding curves and thus resemble closely the field lines of iron filings around a magnet. Similarly, on the limb the chromosphere can be seen as a bright pink rim containing a multitude of small spicules, which are often inclined to an angle of 45° to the limb and represent the fibrils seen in profile on the limb. The spicules owe their shape and configuration to the magnetic field.

Flocculi

Bright pink cloud-like formations denote increased activity and are called flocculi or plages, although the latter term is used to describe corresponding bright areas seen in the line of calcium. They are almost always associated with active sunspot groups. Such flocculi are often seen for a few days before the appearance of a sunspot and may persist for days after the decay of the spot. They surround an active sunspot and extend into its neighbourhood.

Filaments

Perhaps the most outstanding feature of the solar disk in Hα are the long, winding, dark lanes, known as filaments, described by earlier workers as dark flocculi. They are prominences seen on the face of the solar disk, appearing dark in absorption of the hydrogen light emitted by the bright chromosphere. Beyond the limb they are seen in profile as bright hydrogen emission against the dark background of the sky. Hence filaments and prominences are different appearances of the same structure, formed by clouds of material, mostly hydrogen, in the upper chromosphere and

Figure 5. Solar filtergram showing chromospheric network, bright flocculi and dark filaments. 1982 March 2 1015 U.T., 1/30 sec exposure at prime focus on Kodak 2415.

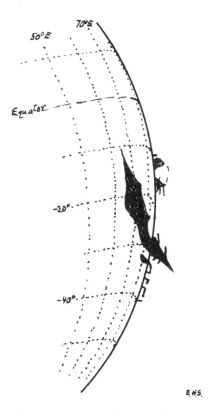

Figure 6. Drawing of a filament near the east limb, seen in continuity with the limb prominence. 1983 April 4 1510 U.T.

inner corona. Quite frequently a limb prominence can be seen in continuity with a filament (Figure 6) confirming that it is one and the same structure. Their behaviour through the cycle corresponds to that of prominences. Quite naturally, filaments change their position on the disk from day to day like sunspots, according to the solar rotation and in doing so their shape changes because of perspective effects: on the centre of the disk they tend to appear as long, dark lanes but near the limb they appear wide and flattened indicating a radial disposition.

The frequency and distribution of filaments is the same as that of prominences. Quiescent filaments can last several solar rotations; they can attain considerable lengths. I have observed some as long as 400,000 kilometres. Typically one side of a filament presents a smooth outline whilst the other is crenated with projections extending towards the chromosphere (Figure 7). Similar structuring is also seen in limb prominences when several arches seem to support the main body of the prominence (Figure 8). Filaments lie along lines separating regions of opposite magnetic polarity. After several rotations such a filament may suddenly darken due to line of sight motion; such a filament surge

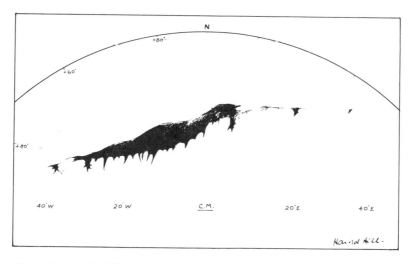

Figure 7. Harold Hill's drawing of a large filament crossing the Sun's central meridian, showing the smooth outline on its north side and crenated projections southwards. 1980 July 28 $L_o=58°.25$ $B_o=+5°.54$.

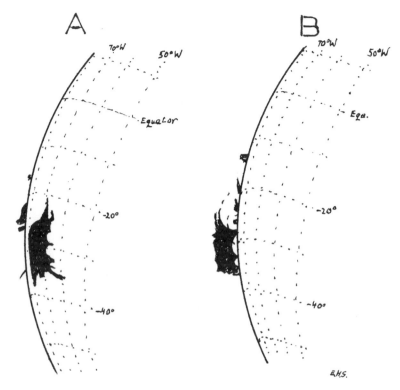

Figure 8. (A) Filament near the south-west limb showing smooth western outline and crenated projections on the opposite side. 1983 April 5 1535 U.T. (B) The same filament appears as a prominence two days later, the crenated projections reaching the chromosphere and forming arch-like formations supporting the main body of the prominence.
1983 April 17 1520 U.T.

corresponds to a prominence eruption on the limb. The filament may then break up and disappear, having been ejected into space; at times it may reappear.

Active region filaments are associated with spot groups but outlive them for several rotations and then tend to shift polewards. In doing so they tilt increasingly towards an east to west direction due to the differential solar rotation and they may eventually form a circumpolar crown.

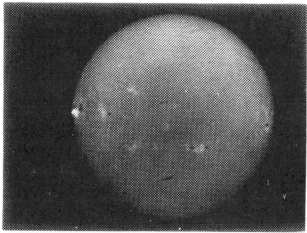

Figure 9. Flare near the east limb. Photograph taken on 1982 June 13 0951 U.T. 1/30 sec exposure at prime focus on Kodak 2415.

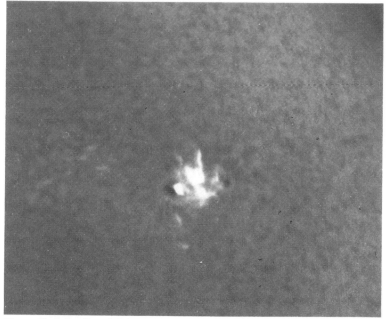

Figure 10. Solar flare: 2B importance. Note brightest part of flare obscuring E-half of the umbra 1985 April 24. 1021 U.T. 1/60 sec exposure at prime focus on Kodak 2415.

Eruptive prominences and filamentous surges are frequently associated with solar flares.

Solar Flares

An intense solar flare is the most dynamic sight an astronomer can witness. A bright flocculus near an active sunspot group may suddenly brighten considerably and become brilliant within a few minutes (Figures 9 and 10). After having reached its maximum it tends to fade much more slowly. The whole event can be as short as 10 to 15 minutes or as long as 4 hours. It may recur in a flare-active region several times until activity dies down. Around the solar maximum period some 20 to 25 flares of varying intensity and extent may occur in one day whilst around minimum they are rare and of lesser intensity. A flare releases an incredible amount of energy in the whole range of the electromagnetic spectrum and has far-reaching effects on the Earth's atmosphere; e.g. the ejection of particles may produce geomagnetic storms and auroræ, the ultraviolet emission causes changes of the conductivity of radiowaves and therefore disturbances in radio communication.

A most intense flare can occasionally be seen in white light, but this is an extremely rare event. The first flare ever recorded was seen in white light by two amateur observers, independently, in 1859: R. Carrington, a brewery manager, and R. Hodgson saw a brilliant white patch of light whilst routinely observing a large sunspot group. How fortunate are today's amateur solar observers in being able to witness much fainter flares with the help of the narrow band filter!

Note. All drawings and photos by the author unless otherwise stated.

ANDREW J. HOLLIS

Photoelectric Photometry: A Quiet Revolution in Amateur Astronomy

Introduction

Much of astronomy, both amateur and professional, consists of making an assessment of the intensity of light. Examples of this include making drawings of the surfaces of the Moon and planets, photographing faint galaxies and nebulæ, or more obviously in estimating the magnitudes of variable stars.

Amateurs tend to make their observations visually but this has limitations. No two observers see colours in the same way or at the same intensity. Though the effects of this can be substantially reduced by using filters, it cannot be totally eliminated. The eye is also a relatively coarse measuring instrument even under ideal conditions. A consistent accuracy of ± 15 percent requires an experienced observer and a star of early spectral type. There is also the major problem of bias, where observers record what they think they see rather than what is there. One has only to think of the canals of Mars, as observed by Percival Lowell at the turn of the century, to appreciate this. Despite this unpromising state of affairs, there is much good and valuable research that can be carried out by the careful visual observer. The pages of the British Astronomical Association Journal demonstrate this in the reports of the observing sections.

When we come to consider photographic observation we find two main advantages over visual techniques. Firstly, the potential for accuracy increases – Walter Pennell's pioneering work in the seventies enabled brightnesses to be estimated to an accuaracy of better than ± 10 percent. Secondly, the record is permanent and measurements can be repeated many times to provide more accurate answers. However, the unsteadiness of the Earth's atmosphere tends to blur fine detail and this is nearly always lost from photographs of the planets.

A third alternative is much newer and has realistically only been available to many amateurs for the last three or four years. It involves making measurements at the telescope using an electronic detector. The technique is known as photoelectric photometry and is already allowing amateurs to make observations on an equal basis with professionals. However, any major advance brings both advantages and disadvantages which need to be considered.

Advantages
An accuracy of measurement of ± 1 percent or better is achievable.
Any form of observer bias is eliminated since the measurements are made electronically.
Observations can be extended into the ultraviolet and infrared by using appropriate detectors and filters.
Results can be transformed to one of the standard systems in use world wide by the correct use of filters.
Results from several observatories, when made on a standard system, can be combined without any loss of accuracy.
The amateur observer can take measurements as accurately as the professional.
The accuracy of the final results does not depend on the size of the telescope used. The author regularly uses a 135 mm aperture reflector and photometry has been done using a 60 mm refractor.

Disadvantages
The equipment is an additional cost. But it is cheaper than the cost of a telescope, much more so if home constructed.
A much more rigorous observing procedure is necessary to achieve maximum accuracy.
Reduction of the readings is a mathematical exercise. It is a trivial exercise for a microcomputer.
The telescope should be accurately driven and aligned to the pole. This requirement is less critical than for photography.
The telescope mounting must be rigid.
Variations in the transparency of the atmosphere limit the accuracy obtainable on a given night.

It is the improvement in the accuracy of observation that has been the biggest attraction for most devotees. Most of the amateurs currently practising PEP (photoelectric photometry) were visual observers of variable stars who were well aware of the likely inaccuracies. The only solution to the problem of inaccuracy is to go photoelectric: One by-product of the increased accuracy is that an observer can follow stars with an amplitude of variation down to 0.02 magnitude. A variation of this amplitude would be undetectable by eye.

Historical Perspective

Photometry is the measurement of light, to be more precise the measurement of the intensity of electromagnetic radiation. This had long been carried out visually by estimating the brightness of the object in question relative to one or preferably more stars of known, constant brightness. In the last century several astronomers introduced instruments which could place an artificial star in the field of view. Adjusting the brightness of this artificial star allowed an estimate of the brightness of the variable to be made by the observer. These instruments were the first photometers.

When light falls on a suitably sensitive surface, electrons are emitted and the 'photoelectric effect' was discovered in 1888. By applying an electrical potential it is possible to collect the electrons for measurement. In 1892 Monck and Fitzgerald, observing from Dublin, used a selenium cell, built by Minchin, to measure the light from Venus, Jupiter and possibly Mars using a 9-inch refractor. By April 1895 the device was sufficiently improved that Wilson, Minchin and Fitzgerald could measure the light of Arcturus. Their report of 1896 gives measures of the brightness of ten stars taken with a 24-inch reflector.

Development proceeded sporadically during the first decades of this century. The major figure during these years was Professor Joel Stebbins who for fifty years from 1907 provided a driving force. He was not a technical innovator himself, but he had the insight to know what was required and who could provide the necessary knowledge. His collaboration with Albert Whitford during the thirties and forties produced many improvements – such as the application of refrigeration to reduce noise in the photometer.

The next advance came just after the Second World War, when Gerald Kron obtained some surplus valves and began experimenting with them. These valves had been used by the British in devices which generated radio noise to jam German communications and were thermionic devices called photomultiplier tubes. PMT's have a detector with amplification of about 10^6 built in. This pioneering work provided the impetus for a generation of professional observers.

The first benefit was the establishment of a standard photometric system. The Johnson and Morgan UBV System was proposed in 1950 and has now been extended to cover UBVRIJKLMNH wavebands. This system, known popularly as the alphabet soup system, defines specific passbands each of which is given a letter. An appropriate choice of detector and filter gives the match to the standard. Another system has also gained a following and this is the 'uvbyβ' system established by Rufener.

Early photoelectric equipment was crude by modern standards and more importantly it was also unreliable. The operator had to diagnose and repair any faults. It was not until the mid-fifties that the reliability had improved sufficiently for the technique to be adopted by most professional institutions. The amateur observer was first encouraged into the field in 1963 with the publication of a book, edited by Frank Bradshaw Wood, describing the construction of suitable equipment. By the late sixties both the AAVSO and the RASNZ were catering for the amateur.

The ready availability of cheap, yet very efficient integrated circuits has provided the impetus for the current interest in photoelectric photometry amongst amateurs. The cheap circuitry available allows the home hobbyist to construct and operate equipment that is both more reliable and also more precise than that available to the professional fifteen years ago. This is changing attitudes in the science as it is an area where amateurs and professionals can meet as equals. The potential for the future is so great that it has been described by Richard Baum as the 'Quiet Revolution'.

The Photometer

The Earth's atmosphere is transparent to light in the visible wavelengths – which explains why our eyes are sensitive to them. However, the atmosphere is also sensitive to other radiation wavelengths which humans cannot detect directly. Whilst the visible band stretches from 400 nm to 700 nm (1 nanometer = 10^{-9} metres = 10 Ångströms), the atmosphere is clear from about 300

Figure 1. The DC photoelectric photometer built by A. J. Hollis shown attached to a 135 mm aperture Newtonian reflector.

Figure 2. Close up of the head assembly of the prototype photometer. The head fixes directly to the eyepiece mounting without any additional bracing or support.

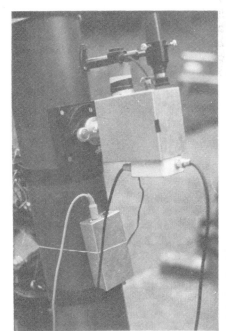

Figure 3. The internal arrangement of the photometer head. The small white package contains silica gel, this dries out the air in the head and dramatically reduces the electronic noise in the photometer.

Figure 4. The remaining electronics is placed on an old tea trolley. Right is the high voltage power supply for the photomultiplier tube; this sits on the counter which gives a visual display of the readings. To the left is a Spectrum microcomputer plus interface and printer, this arrangement does the hard work!

nm (ultraviolet) to 1200 nm (infrared) though the peak transmission is about 550 nm in the green. Beyond this there are windows of various size and transmission in the Intermediate and Far Infrared Microwave, and Radio Bands. At present there are instruments available to amateurs to allow observation between 300 nm and 1200 nm and there are instruments being developed in the USA to extend this from 1200 nm to 2400 nm. Beyond the Infrared bands radio equipment its necessary to detect and analyse radiation.

Photoelectric photometry depends on the so-called 'photoelectric effect'. Some devices change their response when exposed to different intensities of radiation and this can be measured by suitable circuitry. The wavelength that the device responds to depends on the material used and this can be germanium for infrared, silicon in the red, or antimony – caesium for blue or green light.

Many people will have experienced using a photoelectric photometer – perhaps without even realizing it. For example, if you have even used a meter to find the correct exposure setting on your camera then you have measured light levels electronically. The only difference between this and an astronomical photometer is that the astronomical detector is more sensitive and the amplification is higher.

Exposure meters commonly use photodiodes and these devices are used in many other applications, such as in the computer industry.

Most of the detectors used for observations in the blue and visible bands are photomultiplier tubes and these are like the old-fashioned thermionic valve from the days of steam radio. Photodiodes come into their own towards the red and infrared wavebands.

There are a number of discrete components in any photometer. There is a source of radiation, this could be a star, a tumbling asteroid, the Moon, planets or any other object. The radiation is then collected in the telescope which functions just like a bucket gathering photons. The head serves to pass the photons to the detector. The detector converts the radiation into electrical signals which are amplified many thousands of times. These pass to the monitor which converts the signal into a form where it can be recorded perhaps manually, perhaps by a computer.

Let's now look at the instrumentation in more detail.

The Telescope and Mounting

The telescope is not a critical part! The quality of the image it provides is immaterial since its only function is to collect the light and to pass it through a small diaphragm aperture of typically one minute of arc in diameter. The quality of the mounting is of much greater importance. The mounting needs care and attention in construction and setting up as its job is to carry the telescope and photometer head whilst keeping the object under observation central in the diaphragm for perhaps ten minutes. This tracking requirement can cause problems which can usually be solved by some careful work.

Balance is critical. With everything in place – including the photometer head – free the declination axis of the scope. The tube should be balanced so there is no tendency for the tube to rotate under its own weight. As a photometer head weighs a bit less than a camera body one session will allow for both types of observation. Clamp the declination axis and free the polar axis. Carry out the same operation to balance the axis so there is no tendency for the axis to rotate. This can be very difficult to achieve in practice for all orientations of the tube and if this is the case balance at the meridian. Don't forget to reverse the telescope to check both orientations if you use a German equatorial mounting.

When driving there should be a slight positive bias to the balance – achieved using small weights – so that the motor acts as an escapement rather than a driver.

The optics must be collimated, aligned so the optical axis is central to all the optical elements of the telescope. With a Newtonian reflector this means that when you stand back from the eyepiece mount (with no eyepiece in place) you should see the reflection of your eye centrally through the eyepiece mount. Many handbooks describe the process of aligning telescopes and these should be referred to.

Adjusting the orientation of the polar axis is easy but to achieve the best results it can be time consuming. Firstly, align the mounting approximately to the pole – either by sighting on the Pole Star or else by a sensible guesstimate. Accurate alignment can then be achieved by using an eyepiece with illuminated cross wires or by using a bright star that has been defocused to fill the field of a high power eyepiece.

The procedure is as follows:

First examine a star near the Equator and the Meridian.

If the star drifts North	— the Polar Axis points too far West
If the star drifts South	— the Polar Axis points too far East
If the star drift East or West	— the Drive rate is in error

Next examine a star at high declination (45°) and an elevation of about 20°.

If the star drift North	— the Polar Axis points over the Pole
If the star drifts South	— the Polar Axis points under the Pole

The Photometer Head

This part of the system is carried on the eyepiece mount of the telescope. It contains the following elements.

Repeat these steps as often as is necessary. You should try to adjust so that a star will stay central, without guiding, for twenty minutes or longer if possible.

The diaphragm aperture. This is a small hole located at the focus of the telescope. It allows light from the object being measured to pass through whilst excluding light from surrounding stars. In practical terms there is a small area of skylight included and the effect of this must be removed by taking a reading of the adjacent sky with no stars present. Most photometers have a larger aperture as well to allow the observer to centre to object to be observed.

A viewing eyepiece and a flip mirror allow the observer to centre the object in the photometer and then to flip the mirror out of the path to let the light fall on the detector.

A head should contain a Fabry Lens. This is a small lens which enlarges the image of the object on the sensitive surface of the detector. It serves to compensate for any variations in the sensitivity of the surface of the detector.

Filters can be included to allow light from a narrow band of the spectrum to pass. The use of filters allows the observations to be converted to one to the standard systems.

The detector is the heart of any system. It may be a photodiode or a photomultiplier tube. The latter are much easier to deal with though they need care in handling and a power supply of several hundred volts.

Usually the first stages of amplification of the signal are included in the head as well. There are two theories about the nature of light. One theory treats light as a wave motion and the second as a train of particles which are called photons. Each approach can be taken.

A direct current (DC), or analogue, system mimics the wave theory. Its output level is directly proportional to the intensity of the incoming light. The head contains a high gain amplifier and operates in the same way as a camera light meter.

In the pulse-counting system individual photons are amplified and then discriminated. The latter operation sounds grand but just means that any pulses above a preset level are detected and trigger a device which generates a standard pulse. This pulse is usually at a level (called TTL) which is compatable to a computer input.

Electronics

A photomultiplier tube requires a high voltage supply to operate. This is typically several hundred volts. Since it is at one milliamp it is not as bad as it sounds. Suitable circuits have been developed and they can be constructed fairly easily.

The output from the head must be recorded in some way. Early DC systems used a galvanometer and the deflection of the meter was read as the measurement. Even today the individual readings are called deflections. More recently pen chart recorders or voltmeters have been used though sometimes with damping to even out the rapid variations in atmospheric transparency. The modern technique is to use Voltage-to-Frequency conversion. With this technique the output from the head is converted into a string of pulses, whose frequency depends on the level of the input voltage. These pulses can be counted by a frequency meter, a counter or by a computer for as long as is required to take a reading. Pulse-counting systems need a high speed digital counter to record the readings.

SOURCE

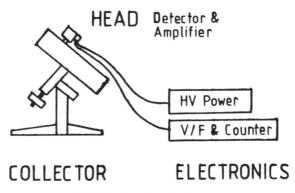

COLLECTOR   ELECTRONICS

Figure 5. Schematic arrangement of a DC photoelectric photometer system.

Data can be written in a log book by hand for reduction later or it can be collected directly by a cheap home microcomputer. This latter has the great advantage that the data can be reduced immediately and the results displayed in real time. The writer uses a 48k Sinclair Spectrum in this way and can confirm that it saves a great deal of time and effort and leaves the observer free to do the astronomy!

Selection of an Observing Programme

Working out what to observe is one of the problems that the beginner has. The first requirement is to gain some experience with handling the equipment to see how it works in service. An observing session or two on a regular but rapid variable star is valuable to check the system is operating satisfactorily. Bright examples of the W Ursæ Majoris class of eclipsing binary stars are a very good choice. These stars have amplitudes of a few tenths of a magnitude and orbital periods of less than a day. With many of this class it is possible to observe either a maximum or minimum of the light curve in a two or three-hour observing run.

Any observing programme must be achievable. Observing a variable with a period of ten days when you have one clear night every ten to fifteen days is unlikely to produce satisfactory results. In areas prone to cloud, such as the UK, the choices are relatively simple. The most likely objects to observe are ones which will produce results either in a single night, single nights spread over a period of months, or else show such little change that they can be observed every ten days satisfactorily.

Many short-period variable stars and most of the minor planets undergo complete or nearly complete light curve cycles during one night. But there are many other phenomena that can be followed, these are observed by high speed techniques. Included in this category are occultations of stars by the Moon or Minor Planets which can be timed to a high degree of precision. There are new fields that have not yet been properly investigated. Among these the most promising appear to be photometry of the lunar surface, the planetary satellites and rings, and perhaps comets. Comets are not easy objects to observe photoelectrically, special filters are necessary and suitable targets are not very frequent.

Long-period variables can be followed photoelectrically but many of them are followed quite adequately by visual observers. There are many semi-regular variables which only vary by two- or three-tenths of a magnitude and these would be a good choice to

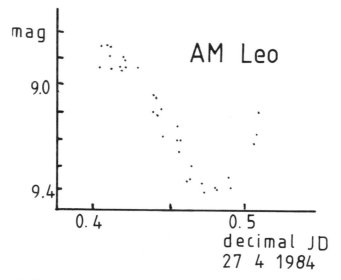

Figure 6. Light curve of AM Leo taken photoelectrically using the 135 mm reflector and DC photometer. Note that the decimal JD (Julian Date) begins at noon.

observe since it is unlikely that these could be followed visually. There are a number of amateurs who have discovered variable stars photoelectrically in recent years. From time to time there are lists of possible variable stars published. Many of these do turn out to be variable and they sometimes have amplitudes of 0.2 magnitudes which are easily detectable.

It is important that observations are used. Many organizations exist which welcome the results of photoelectric photometry and pool the results of many observers. The main organization for this in the UK is the British Astronomical Association. The International Amateur-Professional Photelectric Photometry organization (IAPPP) has acted as the catalyst by encouraging amateurs into the field and by putting them in touch with professional and more advanced amateurs who can give them advice and also make use of the observations they make.

In 1984 the Third European Symposium on Photoelectric Photometry was held at the Royal Greenwich Observatory in Herstmonceux. It was a joint BAA and IAPPP venture and considered a great success by the participants.

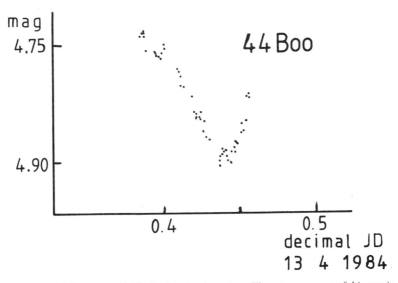

Figure 7. Light curve of 44 Boö taken by the writer. The extreme range of this star is 0.16 magnitudes. An observer trying to follow this star visually would have difficulty in detecting any variation.

There is also the prospect of doing something completely new. In this case it may well be up to the amateur to decide how to analyse the observations and how to publish the results!

Conclusion

The quest for ever larger telescopes and the advance of instrumentation during the first sixty or seventy years of this century tended to take the professional astronomer away from the amateur. He was unable to follow because of the technical sophistication involved and the sheer cost.

The increasing sophistication of electronics and the falling costs have now let amateur acquire equipment that would have not been available to the large institutions only fifteen years ago at any cost.

Photoelectric photometry is now a proven technique that is readily and cheaply available. In these days of budgetary controls, most professionals acknowledge the contributions that can be made by the amateur. In truth there are many professional observing programmes that could not survive without contributions by the amateur. The one that comes immediately to mind is the 'starspot' programme of Dr Douglas Hall of Vanderbilt University in the USA.

Organizations like the BAA and the IAPPP have members who give advice freely on the design, construction and operation of photelectric equipment. A good starting point would be to make contact with the British Astronomical Association at the address given later in this book.

ALAN E. WRIGHT

Radio Stars

As everybody knows, the word 'astronomy' means the study of heavenly bodies, and to many people heavenly bodies means 'stars'. However, there are many other sorts of heavenly bodies, such as planets, nebulæ, galaxies and quasars to name but a few, and, until recently, radio astronomers have paid far more attention to them than to stars.

Our Sun is, of course, a star, and it has received enormous attention from radio astronomers because it is so close. But only in the last decade have large numbers of other radio stars been discovered. And yet today, if one goes as a visitor to a major radio observatory and peers over the shoulders of the astronomer, the odds are high that the names appearing on the computer display screens will be those of familiar stars such as Antares, Mira, Proxima Centauri, or Algol.

How did this come about? Why are observations of radio stars now so important that they take up a large fraction of time on radio telescopes? And what exciting, new discoveries have resulted from these observations?

To start with it's necessary to understand a little of how radio telescopes work and how they detect radio sources.

There are three main types of radio telescope in use: firstly we have the large 'single-dish' instruments such as the Jodrell Bank, 75-metre-diameter telescope, the Algonquin Park 46-metre telescope in Canada or the Parkes 64-metre dish in Australia. These are the 'work horses' of modern radio astronomy – reasonably sensitive, and capable of operating at a wide variety of frequencies. All have featured largely in the detection of radio stars.

Next we have the modern 'arrays'. These are large and, generally, extremely costly instruments consisting of many medium-sized dishes linked together in a precise configuration.

Figure 1 (above) The Parkes 64-metre radio telescope in NSW, Australia, operated by the CSIRO.

Figure 2 (below) The Algonquin Park 46-metre radio telescope in Ontario, Canada, operated by the National Research Council.
Together these giant 'dishes' have been responsible for discovering most of the radio stars known in the Southern and Northern Hemispheres respectively.

They are capable not only of sensitive detections but also of accurately mapping smale-scale details in the radio sources. Probably the best-known example is the Very Large Array in New Mexico. However, perhaps the most important and exciting instrument in this class, soon to be completed, is the array known as the Australia Telescope, which will stretch over 300 kilometres across central New South Wales. These array instruments have had, and probably will have, the greatest impact on stellar radio astronomy.

Finally, we have the telescope technique known as 'very long baseline interferometry' or VLBI for short. For this, individual telescopes are linked across, or even between,continents. Connection by electrical cables or radio links is generally too difficult and so the signals are tape-recorded to be later combined at a processing centre. In this way it is possible to achieve extremely high *resolving powers* of better than one thousandth of a second of arc; meaning that the interferometer's ability to discern fine detail in a radio source is similar to that of a single telescope whose size approaches that of the Earth! At the present time, VLBI links between the continents of Europe, North America, Africa and Australia have been achieved and are becoming commonplace for radio star observations.

Now, although these types of telescope have many important differences they also have an important property in common: they best detect astronomical bodies which are both *hot* and *big:* hot, because the laws of physics say that hot atoms and electrons emit larger quantities of radio energy than cool ones, and big because a radio source produces a larger voltage in the receiving electronics if it fills more of a telescope's beam – i.e. the zone of sky over which a telescope is sensitive.

For the mathematically inclined, the expression for the measured strength of a radio star is:

$$S = 0.1 \ \theta^2 \ T,$$

where we have assumed that observations are being made at a radio frequency of 10 GHz, which is typical for observing radio stars, and that θ is the angular diameter of the radio source in seconds of arc, T is its temperature in degrees Kelvin (K), and S (flux density) is in the radio astronomer's unit of strength, the millijansky (1 mJy is comparable in energy to observing from

Earth a very low-powered CB radio transmitter at the distance of the planet Pluto!).

Let's see what this equation tells us if we apply it to the brightest star in the night sky, Sirius.

As viewed from the Earth, Sirius has an angular diameter of about seven-thousandths of a second of arc, and from its colour we know that its temperature is about 10,000 K. Using our equation we can calculate its flux density as about five-hundredths of a millijansky.

This is very weak indeed – in fact, too weak to be detected. Practical limits for observing radio sources with even the most sensitive radio telescopes are around 1 mJy. Sirius is one of the nearest, hottest, and brightest stars in the sky, so clearly more distant and cooler stars will not be detected!

In order for a star to be detectable with a radio telescope we can now see that it must be either considerably hotter than 10,000 K or have a size of about one second of arc or so.

Are there such stars? Yes, there are – but they are not like ordinary main-sequence stars such as Sirius or the Sun. Once again, as we shall see, radio stronomy has lived up to its reputation for detecting the unusual and bizarre. We shall also see that the properties of 'hotness' and 'bigness' referred to above form a useful basis for dividing the known radio stars into two main groups.

One group has quite ordinary stellar angular sizes but the radio emission we see comes from regions around the stars. These stars have large magnetic fields extending out from them and electrons moving almost at the speed of light spiral around the field lines, producing a radio emission known as synchrotron radiation. These spiralling electrons can produce such enormous energy that the equivalent temperatures as seen at radio frequencies are as much as 10^{10} K. Other radio emission methods sometimes postulated, such as the one known as cyclotron radiation, are even more exotic. These stars, with ordinary angular sizes and very high temperatures (caused by 'non-thermal' emission mechanisms) are referred to as the *non-thermal radio stars*. (The terms synchrotron and cyclotron are used because the radiation is similar to that produced in the terrestrial atom machines of those names.)

The other main group of stars have temperatures similar to those of normal stars (a few thousand degrees) but very large

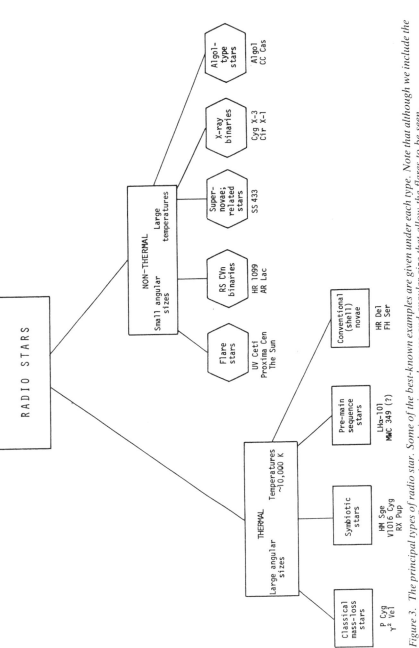

Figure 3. The principal types of radio star. Some of the best-known examples are given under each type. Note that although we include the Sun as a flare star it is only its unique closeness and angular size that allow the flares to be seen.

angular sizes. They are termed the *thermal radio stars,* since their radio emission is that produced by any normal hot body.

To begin with, let's look at some of the *non-thermal* radio stars.

First – and amongst the earliest radio stars to be detected – are the red-dwarf *flare* stars. These were found – using the big dishes at Jodrell Bank and Parkes – to emit quite strong 'bursts' of low-frequency radio waves lasting between a few seconds and several hours. Many, but not all, of these radio 'flares' closely followed flares seen at optical wavelengths. To establish this latter fact, the work of many amateur astronomers in New South Wales and Queensland was of particular value in making optical observations at the same time as the Parkes telescope was taking radio data. We now know that the flare stars so far detected produce energy in a manner somewhat similar to the flares and bursts seen on our Sun but on a much more violent scale. The temperature of this non-thermal radiation often reaches values approaching 10^{16}K.

The second type of non-thermal radio star is the rather grand-sounding group of RS Canum Venaticorum (RS CVn) stars. In line with the normal practice in astronomy, the group is named after its prototype star. Funnily enough, radio emission from RS CVn itself has not yet been detected at radio wavelengths. But this is probably only because the searches are not yet sufficiently sensitive. The strongest star so far measured in this group is a sixth magnitude star in the constellation of Taurus, V711 Tau, which is more often called HR 1099.

In 1978 this object was observed by a group of Canadian radio astronomers as a strong radio source varying rapidly over a few hours at high frequencies.

At the present time, about twenty-five of these RS CVn objects are known. They are all believed to be *binaries* – two stars bound by gravity into a single system. The hotter star is of spectral type F or G and the cooler star of type K. The cooler star has strong emission lines in its optical spectrum of the element calcium. The two stars orbit around each other with a period of only a few days, and must be very close – although not actually in contact as some binaries are. Measurements of the known RS CVn stars have shown us that the radio emission comes from strong magnetic fields in the region around and between the two stars. Why and how such fields exist is not yet known and is the subject of much work at the radio observatories. Perhaps this is one of the problems that will be solved by the extremely high angular resolution of very long baseline interferometry.

Thirdly, we mention in passing what is probably the best-known group of radio stars – the *pulsars*. They were first discovered in 1967. Since then, considerable observational and theoretical work has shown them to be the super-dense neutron cores of dead stars spinning several times a second and emitting beams of radio waves like cosmic searchlights. So much has been written about pulsars that we will say little here except to note that only a few have yet been seen optically. Amongst these the pulsar in the Crab Nebula is easily the brightest and most studied.

Lastly in our list of non-thermal radio stars is the bizarre object know as SS 433. At first glance it is just an an ordinary 14th magnitude star probably connected with the remains of a supernova. However, closer inspection begins to reveal problem after problem. The most astounding is probably that, although SS 433 almost certainly lies in our own Galaxy, it has some emission lines in its optical spectrum shifted so far to the red that we would normally interpret them as belonging to an object lying far out in the Universe. Not only that, but the same spectrum shows lines that are almost equally *blue*-shifted! And, perhaps strangest of all, is the fact that the red- and blue-shifts change in a systematic way from night to night! One explanation for this incredible behaviour has been that SS 433 is a wobbling neutron star (or perhaps even a black hole) emitting gas in two opposing jets at more than one-quarter of the speed of light. We are certainly far from a complete understanding of this peculiar object. At the moment it is unique but the search for similar objects is currently being hotly pursued world-wide.

Now let's look at some of the types of *thermal radio stars*. Firstly, the group I refer to as the *classical mass-loss* stars. This is one group that we now believe we understand fairly well. The classical mass-loss stars are O or B type supergiants whose ultraviolet radiation is so strong that it is blowing off the outer layers of the star's atmosphere.

By the mid-1970s several stars of this type had been detected as radio sources. Examples were P-Cygni, the prototype of all mass-loss stars, and γ^2 Velorum, the bright, Southern Hemisphere object. It was found that the 'hallmark' of this sort of radio star was that their flux densities increased with increasing radio observing frequency in a manner approximately proportional to the frequency to the two-thirds power. This increase was predicted to continue up to infrared frequencies, a prediction that has indeed since been confirmed for several stars. What was the cause of this unusual radio spectrum and what could it tell us about these stars?

An explanation was provided in the mid-70s by theoretical astronomers: gas flows out from the star, getting thinner and more extended, with its density dropping as the square of its distance from the central star. The strong flux of ultraviolet radiation from the hot star strips off the electrons from their parent hydrogen and helium atoms. It is these hot electrons that emit radio radiation as they pass close to a 'stripped' atom. And it is this large, ionized atmosphere that makes it possible to detect these stars and gives rise to the particular form of the radio spectrum that was observed. Furthermore, and more important, it was also shown that accurate flux measurements could lead to more accurate determinations of mass-outflow rates than those obtainable by other, optically based methods. Such rates are crucial to the understanding of how massive stars evolve and how galaxies behave in the early days after their formation.

As radio observations became more sensitive and the searchers for new radio star detections were intensified in the late-1970s, it became clear that several objects did *not* have the simple radio spectrum predicted by the theoreticians. In particular several stars were found whose flux densities increased too quickly with increasing frequency to be explained by the simple model. Furthermore these same stars had optical spectra considerably more complex than those of the classical mass-loss stars and many were in fact of the type known as *symbiotic* (the word 'symbiosis' means 'living together in a mutually beneficial partnership').

Symbiotic stars have optical spectra that show evidence of an extremely hot star (about 100,000 K) and a very cool star (about 3000 K). Several of these stars are known to have had a spectacular brightening of their optical magnitudes in the last few decades. One of the most recent to flare into prominence is the object known as HM Sge.

Perhaps the majority of astronomers now believe that symbiotic systems are in fact made up of two stars – one hot and one cool – 'living together' in a binary star system. Alternative theoretical models have been put forward from time to time in which just one star is able to maintain both very hot and very cold conditions near its surface, but radio observations are now beginning to show that such 'single-star' models are unlikely to be correct.

The picture which is now emerging is of a giant, red, Mira-like star whose strong infrared radiation drives dust grains from the star's surface out into space. As the grains are blown out, they collide with the gas of the star's atmosphere and cause it to flow out too. This gas is first ionized by strong ultraviolet radiation from a companion white dwarf star and then is gravitationally pulled on to, or at least very close to, the hot star's surface. The release of gravitational energy is the basic reason for both the extremely strong ultraviolet radiation from the white dwarf and the rapid optical brightening. However, recent radio observations have shown that the situation may be even more complex, with a second 'star wind' blowing out from the white dwarf star and colliding with the cool star wind. It may well be that radio observations will be able to disentangle the complicated interactions in the symbiotics.

A short article such as this cannot hope to convey all the excitement that at present prevades the study of the radio emission from stars. I have not even mentioned several of the groups of radio stars that we know about except to show them in Figure 3. Much of our current theoretical understanding will probably turn out to be wrong – no doubt some of the problems we have in fitting some stars into the existing groups arise because the stars are of a new, as yet unrecognised, type. However, as a radio astronomer, I feel particularly satisfied that we can at last justify our name by making an important contribution to the study of what has previously been the sole province of the optical astronomer – those most important of heavenly bodies, the stars themselves.

DAVID L. BLOCK

Spiral Galaxies, Side by Side

In trying to classify the myriad of spiral galaxies into discrete 'bins', the classification scheme of Hubble serves as an excellent springboard.

Hubble had noticed that some spiral galaxies had very large bulges, while others had small or even semi-stellar bulges; in some galaxies the arms were seen to be tightly wound around the bulge, whereas in others, a far more open pattern was presented; thirdly, while few if any stars could be seen in the arms of some spirals, in others, the arms could be resolved into myriads of stars and ionized hydrogen regions.

Prototypes of Hubble's Sa, Sb, and Sc galaxies are illustrated in 'The Hubble Atlas'. In this paper, we shall confine our discussion primarily to the Sc variety: small bulge and open, well resolved arms.

The size of a galaxy on a photographic plate does not tell one anything about its true linear size in light years. A good example is Messier 33. While that galaxy spans one degree in the sky, it would of course be completely erroneous to conclude that it is a large galaxy – it is merely close by.

The same is true for other members of our Local Group – the Large and Small Magellanic Clouds, NGC 6822 and IC 1613. At nearby distances ranging from 0.05 Mpc to 0.8 Mpc, their linear diameters only range from 2 kpc to 10 kpc.

Since dwarf and extreme dwarf systems are so completely over-represented in our Local Group, great care has to be taken in comparing distance indicators in the nearby systems to those far out.

In this context, the Swiss astronomer G. Tammann has remarked that if the ionized hydrogen regions of the nearby dwarf

Virgo cluster. Observed redshifts can fail to be accurate indicators of distance in such cases for two reasons:

1. We are falling toward the Virgo cluster with a velocity of 280 km/s and
2. Owing to motions within the cluster itself, amounting to several hundred km/s.

For the Virgo cluster, all galaxies were printed with a velocity v = 1100 km/s, corresponding to a distance of 20 Mpc.

As for distant spirals, the darkroom had to be large, with the enlarger near the top of the ceiling and the photographic paper on the floor!

The Photographs and the Darkroom Runs

With a range in redshift of z = 0.004 to z = 0.030, the sample was divided into two groups:

Group 1

Those galaxies with redshifts in the range z = 0.004 up to, but not including, z = 0.012, were photographed from Schmidt films at a frame height of 9mm, using a 75mm lens and light table attached to the Polaroid MP–3 multi-purpose system at the South African Astronomical Observatory in Cape Town.

Group 2

Group 2 galaxies, with redshifts in the remaining interval z = 0.012 to z = 0.030, were photographed at a higher magnification, at a frame height 3 mm, employing a 35 mm lens, and the same Polaroid MP–3 system.

Calibration of scale between Groups 1 and 2, and in printing the entire sample, was effected by photographing a millimetre ruler at the side of every negative.

While the majority of the galaxies could be accomodated on a 5″ × 7″ photographic paper format, only the intrinsically large ones required a 10″ × 8″ format. Polyethelene laminated paper was used, either on a pearl, or semi-matt finish. The grade found best suited to our purposes was grade 4.

A typical darkroom (printing) run would result in not more than five galaxy photographs; all unacceptable prints were rejected, until an optimum quality was reached.

Exposure times at the enlarger – for the different heights,

galaxy IC1613 were directly compared to those of M101, th
would have a distance underestimated by a factor of 10.

In the years 1976-80, the author began and comp
programme of preparing photographs of galaxies not just
in the night sky, but where the degree of enlargement was r
to the galaxy redshift, assuming, of course, the redshift
valid indicator of distance. In this work, a Hubble consta
kms^{-1} Mpc^{-1} is used throughout, although the actual value
is not relevant as far as making comparisons in the linear
galaxies is concerned; the diameters all scale up o
accordingly, depending on whether a smaller or larger
constant is used; the comparison ratio between diameters
the same.

Thus, a galaxy with a redshift of 0.016 (correspondi
recession velocity v of 4800 km/s) would be enlarged four
much as one with a redshift of $z = 0.004$, $v = 1200$ k
galaxies would then appear on the identical physical scal

In our study, the redshift limits were taken to be 0.
0.030; the lower limit was placed to minimize the effect of
motions on the diameters, while the upper one was chose
arbitrarily) to ensure that distant galaxies were not over-er
still to have well-defined resolution.

Pertaining to random motions, suppose a galaxy
observed Hubble velocity of 1200 km/s ($z = 0.004$), wh
true Hubble velocity due to the expansion of the
corresponds to a redshift of $z = 0.003$, owing to a randon
of 300 km/s in the line of sight. Then

$$\frac{\text{Printed diameter}}{\text{True diameter}} = \frac{1200}{900}$$

$$= 1.33$$

so that, in this instance, the printed diameter is 33 per ce
than the actual diameter. Velocity errors or random mo
thus produce a gigantic change in the linear diameters fo
spirals. The percentage errors do, however, scale dow
with increasing redshift.

We also remark that particular care has to be tak
printing galaxies in gravitationally bound systems, suc

depending on the galaxy's redshift – were co-ordinated using a light-sensitive CDS meter.

The photographs were then mounted individually on cards, so as to enable flexibility in classification, and sequencing the galaxies in order of different properties: linear diameters, arm widths,....

The Surveys Used

The surveys used for this study were, firstly, the Palomar Sky Survey. This is a two-colour blue/red survey, and contains 935 areas, each 6 × 6 degrees, covering the entire northern sky, and the southern sky down to – 30 degrees. (There is an extension for objects further south, known as the Whiteoak Extension, but it is in red only, and extends down to – 42 degrees).

For the southern skies, we made extensive use of the UK Schmidt IIIa-J film survey. The UK 1.2–m (48-inch) Schmidt is in most respects an exact copy of the 1.2–m at Palomar, but the fainter limiting magnitude of 23^m is made possible by the use of special sensitised IIIa-J emulsions. Each plate in that Survey covers 6.5 × 6.5 degrees; 606 fields are required to cover the southern sky south of −20 degrees.

For some galaxies, use was also made of the 'Quick Blue' Survey of the European Southern Observatory.

The technique of printing galaxies on a uniform linear scale is illustrated in Figure 1, where a photograph of the well-known spiral M81 appears together with one of the galaxy NGC 3646. What the photographs tell us is that if the distances to these two galaxies is correct, as determined from Cepheid variables and the redshift respectively, then M81 is actually so small, compared to NGC 3646, that it would only occupy that galaxy's nucleus! (The discrepancy in size could be larger if M81 is taken to be at a closer distance as suggested by observations of that galaxy's planetary nebulae!).

Figure 2 is a composite of some other well-known spirals and includes M83, M101 and NGC 1232, all on the same scale.

The 'Standard Candle' Problem

One of the most fundamental problems in extragalactic astronomy is to try and determine the rate at which the Universe expands – the Hubble constant. Such determinations have direct implications not only for the size of the observable Universe, but also regarding limits as to its age.

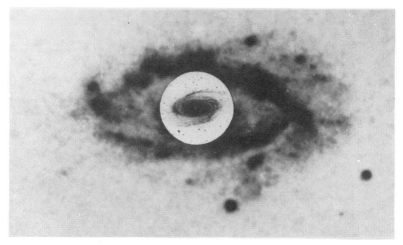

Figure 1. The very well-known spiral galaxy M81 printed on the same linear scale as NGC 3646.

The Palomar prints of M81 and NGC 3646 are copyright © 1960 National Geographic Society – Palomar Sky Survey, and are reproduced by permission of the California Institute of Technology.

To this end, astronomers have concentrated on finding galaxies which have constant intrinsic brightness – what we shall hitherto refer to as 'standard candles'. For, if such objects exist, it is a very simple matter to compute the distance to that object using light's inverse square law behaviour; knowing the distance and measuring the galaxy's speed of recession v (from a spectrum), the Hubble constant H is obtained from

$$\log\langle H\rangle = 0.2\langle M\rangle + \langle b\rangle + 5$$

where M and m are the absolute and apparent magnitudes of the galaxy, and

$$\langle b\rangle = \langle \log v - 0.2m\rangle$$

The brackets ⟨H⟩ denote the average Hubble constant, obtained by observing a large sample of galaxies.

Examples used to date have been ScI spiral galaxies (see below), and the brightest elliptical members in clusters.

It is curious to find that one of the more fundamental questions that one may ask about spiral galaxies has met with surprising

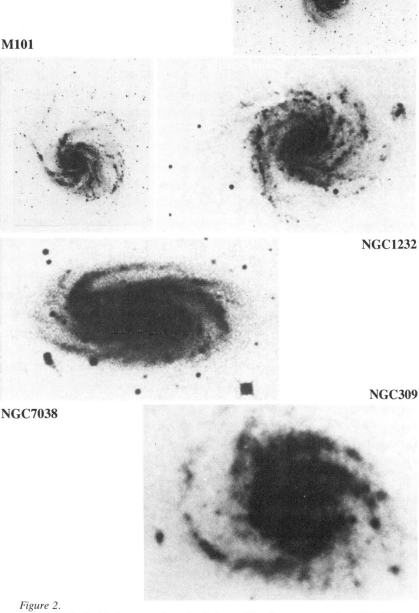

M83

M101

NGC1232

NGC309

NGC7038

Figure 2.
  All galaxies in this figure are from the Palomar Blue Survey, except for NGC 7038.
Palomar photographs are copyright © 1960 by the National Geographic Society –
Palomar Sky Survey, and are reproduced by permission of the California Institute of
Technology. UK Schmidt photographs are copyright © The Royal Observatory,
Edinburgh. Original negative of NGC 7038 from UK Schmidt Telescope unit.
Reproduced by permission.

neglect: the question is simply: 'Are there ranges in the linear diameters of spiral galaxies all assumed to be standard candles? Moreover, do such objects (at least for spirals) really exist?'

The Van Den Bergh Galaxy Classification Scheme

One of the most perceptive classification schemes in trying to find standard candles, whereby galaxies would be grouped into discrete *luminosity* bins, was published some twenty-six years ago by the Dutch-Canadian astronomer S. van den Bergh.

At looking at scores of photographs of spiral galaxies on the Palomar Sky Survey, van den Bergh noticed that some Sc spirals had long, well-developed arms; others presented a far shorter, scraggy spiral-arm appearance. Those with well-developed, long arms were grouped into class I; those with shorter arms into classes II, III, and so on.

Prototypes of ScI (i.e. Hubble type c and van den Bergh class I) galaxies are illustrated in Figure 2. The classic nearby ScI spiral is Messier 101, or NGC 5457.

In that spiral, the long arms cover a *very small* percentage of the total optical disk; such arms are appropriately termed *filamentary*. In contrast, spiral arms which cover a large percentage of the disk (such as in Messier 33, NGC 598) are called *massive*.

The key point here is that any Sc spiral with a morphological appearance akin to M101 would be binned into the same *luminosity* bin as M101 i.e. it would be assumed to have the same luminosity as M101.

But do such objects exist?

Our knowledge as of 1975 both for brightest cluster members, and for spiral galaxies, was a decided *yes*. Standard candles would have to have very much the same linear size. It *was*, of course, known at that stage, that galaxies themselves came into a large range of physical sizes, but the standard candle sub-group was assumed to exist.

The Large Range in the Linear Diameters of Galaxies

As far as elliptical galaxies are concerned, one need only think of the dwarf dE class (introduced by Baade and Wilson; the companions to the Virgo spiral M100 serve as good examples) and compare them to the giant/supergiant cD systems, ranging in size from about three times the size of the Milky Way, 3×30 kpc, to over 2,000,000 parsecs! The term cD galaxy (introduced by astronomers Matthews, Morgan and Schmidt) describes a galaxy with the nucleus of a giant elliptical, and surrounded by a very extended, slowly decreasing surface brightness envelope. cD galaxies constitute by far the largest galaxies known.

In the case of *spirals,* the range in physical size was generally thought to be far more restricted; many an astronomical student today would cite M81, M31, and M101 as typically large spirals within Hubble types b and c.

Interestingly enough, prior to 1976, no *systematic* study of the physical appearance of spiral galaxies on a uniform physical scale had been undertaken.

When the author examined some ScI spirals in this way, some were found to be considerably smaller (in kpc) than others. Not only were ranges in linear diameter for this "standard candle" subgroup apparent (from 30 kpc to 90 kpc), but other astrophysically important variations as well – specifically, variations in the linear width of the arms from one spiral to the next. No quantitative uniformity was seen.

At about the same time, A. Sandage and G. Tammann took photographs of many different galaxies in the compilation of their Revised Shapley-Ames Catalogue. They found that in classifying ScI's and then computing their absolute magnitudes for this much larger sample, the spread in absolute magnitude was very large.

What then did bright ScI spirals have that faint ScI spirals did not? The answer came almost simultaneously, but completely independently, from R. Kennicutt, in Minnesota, and the author.

Bright Sc spirals had *linearly wide arms:* faint Sc spirals had *linearly narrow* arms. A strong correlation was found between *linear arm width* and *blue absolute magnitude,* as seen in Figure 3.

This is well illustrated in the comparison of two ScI spirals M101 and NGC 309 (Figure 2); NGC 309 is a very luminous spiral, being 1.8 magnitudes brighter than M101; the spiral arms of NGC 309 are wider than those in M101 by a factor of 4.

If we assume that distant ScI's (such as NGC 309) are of the same brightness as M101, a serious *underestimate of distance* would result.

The inference is that, as far as spiral galaxies are concerned, standard candles – whether defined as spirals which have the same absolute brightness, or same physical appearance (linear diameter, linear arm width...) – do not exist. Astrophysically, each one is seen to differ from the next.

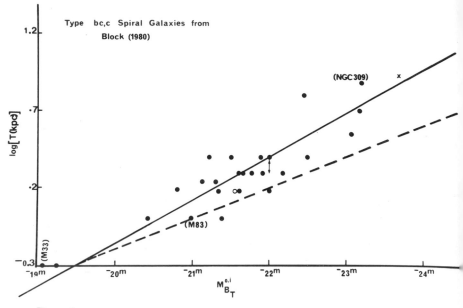

Figure 3.
Reproduced by permission from the journal 'Astronomy and Astrophysics'.

Before concluding this section, it should be remarked that while there is a very tight correlation between the linear size of a galaxy and its absolute magnitude, there are exceptions; care does have to be exercised. Not all high luminosity galaxies are intrinsically large; a good example is M83, where use of a standard absolute magnitude – diameter formula gives a distance to that galaxy of beyond the Virgo cluster (which, as we know, is completely absurd). Nevertheless, it is *generally* true to say that objects of the same luminosity would have about the same linear diameters.

A Discussion of some Photographic Pairs

Figure 4
In this composite of Messier 33, and NGC 3646, we firstly compare the visual, or morphological appearance. The arms are in both instances *massive* (as compared to *filamentary* arms), covering much of the total optical disk. The luminosity class of

M33

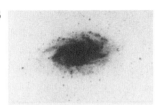

NGC3646

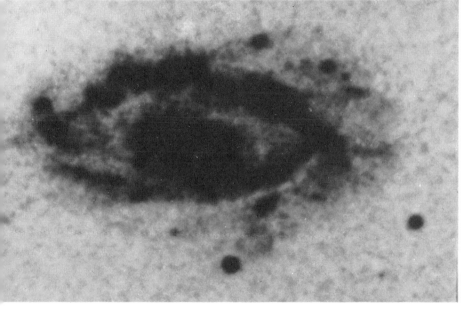

Figure 4.
Photographs in this figure are copyright © 1960 National Geographic Society –
Palomar Sky Survey, and are reproduced by permission of the California Institute of
Technology.

M33 is II–III; that of NGC 3646 only half a class up (II). M33 is of
Hubble type c, NGC 3646 of type bc, so that both these two
galaxies have almost identical morphological classifications:

M33: Sc II–III
NGC 3646: Sbc II

On a uniform linear scale, however, M33 is *quantitatively* so
different from NGC 3646; from the linearly thin arms of M33 to
the linearly very thick arms of NGC 3646.

Figure 5

The well-known southern spiral M83 has a morphological appearance much akin to that of the galaxy NGC 309. Both these galaxies have almost identical pitch angles for their spiral arms, and in many ways NGC 309 is simply a much larger version of M83. Undoubtedly *some* of the difference in appearance of the arms is a resolution effect, with NGC 309 seventeen times as far away as M83.

The arms of NGC 309 are indeed exceptionally wide: this galaxy is also one of the brightest in the Revised Shapley-Ames Catalogue – and fits in with the absolute magnitude-arm width correlation discussed above.

Figure 6

NGC 2082 and NGC 7038 on the same scale. These two galaxies have almost identical luminosity classes: II–III for NGC 2082, 1.8 for NGC 7038, but they have a difference in linear arm width of 3 kpc. The point again to be made is that galaxies can be qualitatively so similar, quantitatively so different.

Our Milky Way Galaxy is of the same Hubble type as NGC 7038 – type bc, luminosity class II. Its appearance would be similar to NGC 7038, but much smaller. Assuming the redshift to be a valid distance indicator, with a Hubble flow characterized by $H = 55$ kms^{-1} Mpc^{-1}, these photographs would confirm that by no means is the diameter of the Milky Way "representative" of any typical bc, c spiral (as is stressed in many textbooks and photographic overlays of the Milky Way and NGC 1232); the Milky Way's arms simply fit in to the range of arm widths allowed within the bc, c classes.

From our absolute magnitude – linear arm width relation, if we assume an absolute magnitude for our Galaxy of -20.5, that relation predicts an arm width of some 800 parsecs; this is consistent with the width of the local arms as estimated from the distribution of young clusters.

For further examples of photographs of spiral galaxies on the same scale, the reader is referred to the author's Atlas, 'A Photographic Atlas of primarily late type spirals printed as if each galaxy were at the same distance', published by the University of Fort Hare Press, 1984.

The High Surface Brightness Spirals

An extremely interesting sub-group in our study are those galaxies

**M83 and NGC 309 printed
on the same Physical Scale**

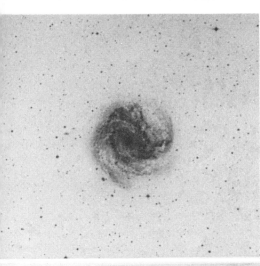

NGC309

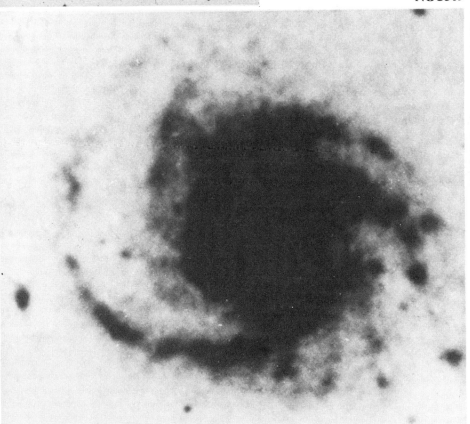

Figure 5.
   Photograph of M83 reproduced by permission of the European Southern Observatory from their 'Quick Blue' Survey. Photograph of NGC 309 is copyright © 1960 National Geographic Society – Palomar Sky Survey and is reproduced by permission of the California Institute of Technology.

NGC2082

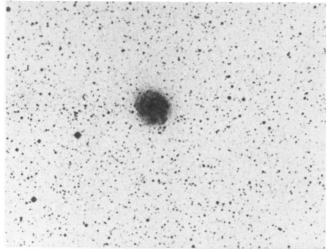

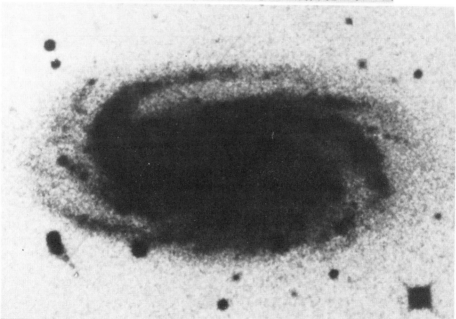

NGC7038

Figure 6.
  Photograph of NGC 2082 is reproduced by permission of the European Southern Observatory. Photograph of NGC 7038 is copyright © The Royal Observatory, Edinburgh. Original negative by UK Schmidt Telescope Unit.

which present a predominantly saturated, black image on the IIIa–J Survey (figure 7). In order to show the spiral structure, not seen on the J-Survey, the galaxies in Figure 7 are arranged in upper and lower pairs; the (B) photographs which do show the spiral arms come from the ESO B Survey, except for the one of M83 at lower right, which is from the Palomar Blue Survey.

We begin our discussion by considering NGC 6215. This spiral is at a very low galactic latitude (of only $-9°$), as is evidenced by the numerous Milky Way stars in the foreground. Because of this, the surrounding envelope probably extends much further than seen in Figure 7.

M83 is unusual in several respects; it is one of the *most blue spirals known,* having a remarkable ultraviolet minus blue $(U-B)$ excess for its value of blue minus visual $(B-V)$; its central surface brightness is also very high. In the literature, we have descriptions of M83 as being 'giant', 'supergiant' and 'larger than our own Galaxy', which, of course, is not correct.

M83 is surrounded by a very extensive envelope of neutral hydrogen gas – the envelope extends to nearly ten times the optical diameter of 22 kpc, out to 200 kpc!

Curious outer morphology is evident in NGC 6221; almost the resemblance of some 'bow-wave', with the galaxy moving through intergalactic matter

The smallest type c in our high surface brightness spiral sub-group is NGC 2082, also illustrated in Figure 7. Its diameter is only some 7 kpc. (Spiral structure is known to occur on even smaller linear scales! In NGC 3928, for example, the spiral structure extends from only 350 parsecs to just over 1 kpc).

An interesting observation about this group of galaxies presenting saturated/nearly saturated images on the IIIa–J Survey is that *none of them seem to have linearly wide arms.*

Toward The Future

Theory versus Observation
The normal density wave theory of spiral galaxies treats spiral arms as a gaseous phenomenon. It predicts that in massive galaxies the spiral shock is stronger and narrower than in less massive galaxies.

The spiral arms which we photograph, however, are not made of gas but of stars. What does the theory therefore predict?

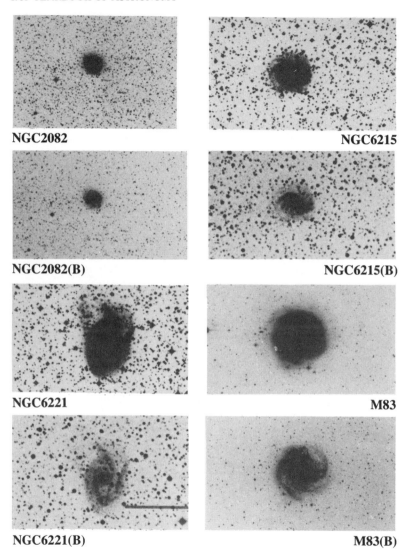

Figure 7.
UK Schmidt photographs are copyright © The Royal Observatory, Edinburgh. The original negatives are from the UK Schmidt Telescope Unit, and are reproduced by permission. ESO B–photographs are reproduced by permission of the European Southern Observatory. The Palomar print of M83 is copyright © 1960 National Geographic Society – reproduced by permission of the California Institute of Technology.

If the spiral shock represents the location of stellar birth then massive galaxies, which have a shorter rotation period at the same radius compared to less massive galaxies, should show broad stellar arms with a narrow dust lane at the shock. (This does, of course assume that a more massive galaxy has more mass inside the same radius as a less massive one).

Conversely, less massive galaxies would have weak and broad shock fronts with star formation of, presumbly, rather low efficiency and, owing to their small mass and slow rotation speeds, the massive stars born in the arms would not move far in their lifetimes and the arms would be massive but linearly narrow.

This does tie in with our findings described above, except that the spiral arms of M33 should originate from weak shock fronts; those of M83 from weak shock fronts as well; those of NGC 309 from strong shocks (as its arms are filamentary) but those of NGC 3646 from weak shocks (as its arms are massive), so that the normal density-wave theory seemingly cannot be correct.

In a modification, Drs Leisawitz and Bash have computed the trajectories of giant molecular clouds (GMCs) born in the shock wave, and examined their destruction and the locations of the stars which form from them. Their work predicts that for galaxies with a specified central mass concentration (e.g. the Sc's), what determines the linear width of the arms is whether the spiral is of a high *mass* (their HM models) or a low *mass* (the LM models).

This ties up very well with our work: in collaboration with Dr Huchtmeier, the author has examined linear arm width as a function of the parent galaxy's HI mass. NGC 2082 (Figure 6), for example, has a HI mass at least 98 per cent lower than that of NGC 309 (Figure 5). Figure 8 shows our correlation, where late-type spirals with a systematically larger HI content also have the linearly wider arms.

The results of Leisawitz and Bash only apply to those galaxies which do admit a density wave, and further work is clearly needed for those which do not.

Perhaps one of the key conclusions from the present work, as far as modelling at least late-type spirals is concerned, is the following: 'Luminosity type I galaxies should be modelled so as to be able to accommodate both linearly wide and linearly narrow arms. Likewise for lower luminosity class spirals, such as II, II – III.'

Photographs such as plate 6, of NGC 2082 and NGC 7038, emphasize that the spiral arms of galaxies having the same degree of

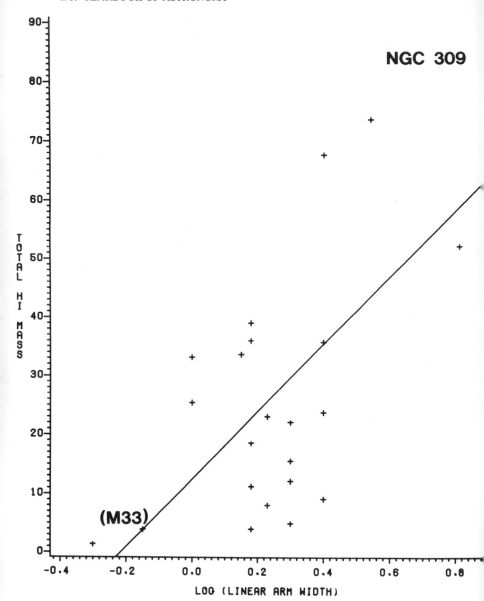

Figure 8.

development (surface brightness, and arm/interarm contrast) can be *both* linearly narrow and wide.

Arms which are linearly narrow belong to those galaxies which do not rotate as fast at the same radius as those which have wide arms; it is thus all the more curious that the arms in both cases can still have the same degree of development.

It is important to see that arm widths are starting to be incorporated into present-day theoretical models, based on the empirical data as to what spiral galaxies actually look side by side.

I conclude with a thought provoking statement made to me last year by an astronomer in Edinburgh who, after examining the photographic evidence of the large difference in galaxy sizes whose distances we know from Cepheids, and whose distances we compute from the redshift, pronounced:

'The Hubble Constant must be 100!'

GARRY E. HUNT

Uranus: Voyager is Coming

1. Introduction

Recent investigations have shown that the major planets, Jupiter, Saturn, Uranus, and Neptune, form two separate families of planets in the outer Solar System. Jupiter and Saturn have similarities in their overall composition and physical properties with their atmospheric compositions similar to that on our Sun. Uranus and Neptune may be different with less than solar proportions of the light elements and larger proportions of the heavier materials such as methane. To account for these basic differences there are essential steps into formally understanding the origin of the Solar System. However, Uranus may be an important planet in the celestial jigsaw which is still relatively unkown in much of its basic properties and therefore is full of intrigue.

Uranus is the seventh planet of the Solar System, discovered in 1781 by Sir William Herschel while he was making a telescopic survey of the heavens. While Herschel's skill as an observer has been demonstrated by his discovery of Uranus, it was his heroic endurance that astonished visitors to his home. One of them wrote '... I went to bed about one o'clock and up to that time he had found that night four or five new nebulæ. The thermometer in the garden stood at 13°F, but in spite of this Herschel observes the whole night through except that he stops every three or four hours and goes into the room for a few moments ...'

While the discovery of Uranus was in itself a landmark in planetary astronomy, the limited knowledge of the planet and its surrounding environment has demonstrated it to be a strange object. In particular, the axial inclination of Uranus is unique in the Solar System. At an angle of 98° it makes the planet's rotation technically retrograde. The axis is essentially in the plane of the orbit so that twice during each orbit of the Sun the axis is at right angles to the direction of the Sun. In between these times one or other of the poles directly faces the Sun, and this year the north pole will be in this position.

At a distance of nearly 20 AU, it is very difficult to detect details in the atmosphere, or resolve the disk at sufficiently high spectral and spatial resolution to determine the basic compositional and structural properties of the planetary system. We do not know yet, with precision, the rotation rate of the planet or any properties of its meteorological system. The discovery of the ring systems in 1977 was another major step in our knowledge, but their composition, the possibility of trapped satellites in the rings and further ringlets have all to be investigated. The satellites of Uranus, currently no more than point sources of light, can only be described in general terms. The first part of this article discusses the current understanding of Uranus and sets the scene for the encounter by the Voyager 2 spacecraft in January 1986. This event will suddenly create an explosive growth in our understanding of Uranus as the planet, satellites, and rings suddenly become worlds of their own.

2. Current Knowledge of Uranus

2.1 Structure and Composition

Uranus (and Neptune too) are smaller and colder than their giant companions Jupiter and Saturn (Table 1). In fact, Uranus has 15 per cent more mass than the Earth and only 5 per cent the mass of Jupiter. However, with a density of 1.2 g cm^{-3} this planet (and Neptune) is denser than the larger gas giants. While Jupiter and Saturn are largely composed of hydrogen and helium, Uranus and Neptune probably consist of heavier materials such as oxygen, nitrogen, carbon, silicon, and iron. Uranus is believed to have a three-part internal structure with a rocky core of heavy elements, then a mantle of water, methane and ammonia, with a low density crust of hydrogen and helium. It is anticipated that convective processes in the interior would lead to the production of a magnetic field. Some observations at ultraviolet wavelengths have been suggestive of auroral activities as a consequence of the detection of intense H-Lyman α and H_2 emission from the planet, and also consistent with the presence of a magnetic field whose positive detection must await the forthcoming Voyager investigations (see Section 3).

TABLE 1

Physical Data on the Outer Planets

	Earth	Jupiter	Saturn	Uranus	Neptune
Mean Distance from Sun (AU)	1	5.2	9.5	19.1	30
Period of Revolution	365.26 (d)	11.86 yrs	29.46 yrs	84.01 yrs	164.8 yrs
Rotational Period	$23^h\ 56^m\ 4^s$	$9^h\ 55^m\ 29^s$	$10^h\ 39^m$	$15 - 178^h$	$\sim 18h$
Mass (Earth = 1)	5.97×10^{24} kg	317.89	95.18	14.6	17.2
Equatorial Radius	6378	71,400	60,330	26,200	24,750
Mean Density $(g\ cm^{-3})$	5.5	1.3	0.7	1.2	1.7
Volume (Earth = 1)	1	1316	755	67	57
Oblateness	0.003	0.06	0.1	0.01 – 0.03	?

There is conclusive evidence that Jupiter, Saturn, and Neptune each possess internal heat sources which relate to some residual heat remaining from the time of formation of the planet, together with a small component arising from the gravitational contraction of the planet. Uranus presents a major difficulty when we try to establish a tidy theory to explain all these objects. The accuracy of our current measurements suggest that the effective temperature of Uranus is 58 ± 2 k, which is essentially the same as the black body temperature expected for the planet. This situation must then relate to interior processes which differ for Uranus, compared with the other planets. Furthermore, there will be consequential differences in the weather systems of their planetary atmospheres, with only Uranus not receiving an additional contribution in the driving mechanisms from internal heating. The planetary radiation budget will be a crucial future spacecraft observation.

2.2 Atmosphere

The atmospheres of the giant outer planets are hydrogen-rich reducing envelopes in contrast to the oxidizing atmospheres of the terrestrial planets. The spectrum of Uranus is dominated by hydrogen and strong methane absorptions, particularly in the red and infrared portions of the spectrum. It is the absorption of sunlight by the methane that gives Uranus its familiar bluish-green colour. Very few other constituents have yet been detected in the Uranian atmosphere. We anticipate helium to be present, but the precise amount is totally unknown. Traces of deuterium, in the form of HD and CH_3D have been detected spectroscopically using terrestrially based telescopes. The accuracy of these data does not yet warrant extensive analyses of the D/H ratio for Uranus. This will, or course, be an important parameter to derive from future more accurate measurements as a result of its cosmological significance.

Ammonia has not been detected spectroscopically at visible wavelengths, while at microwave wavelengths, which probe to deeper levels in the atmosphere, the measurements suggest that there is less than would be expected in a mixing ratio based upon solar abundances. Curiously, the entire microwave region (in the neighbourhood of 1 cm) is found to have a temperature of 50 K or more higher than the condensation temperature of ammonia. Thus gaseous ammonia in vapour pressure equilibrium with solid ammonia is not the characteristic of the entire planet. However, it is difficult to imagine why Uranus is in this state. It is possible that this depletion of ammonia may be due to the formation of NH_4SH clouds at lower levels in the atmosphere. This hypothesis would then require the atmosphere to have a ratio of S to N which is enhanced relative to the solar abundance. While the presence of sulphur in the atmosphere (of all the major planets) is thought to originate through H_2S, its detection has still to be confirmed.

Radio astronomers have now been monitoring the micro-wave spectrum of Uranus for several years, and have found that the greatest variability occured between 1965 and 1971, and that the secular increase in temperature reported during the past 15 years has now been reversed. Temperature maps at 6 cm show an increase in temperature between equator and pole with some evidence for a warm ring surrounding the north pole of the planet, which is the sunlit pole. This spatially variable brightness distribution may be responsible for the observed variability of the microwave spectrum.

The Uranian atmosphere may at first appear to be deep and relatively clear from major cloud layers. We may anticipate layers of photochemical particulates, but any major cloud system could well be at a relatively deep level. The upper cloud levels are likely to be composed of methane at these cold outer reaches of the Solar System, with ammonia and complicated compounds of ammonia forming the deeper layers (Figure 1). Quite different from the colourful and visually active giant Jupiter!

2.3 *Atmospheric Motions*

Uranus is the first planet so far from the Earth that dynamical activity, manifested by clouds, cannot be easily observed by ground-based observations. Consequently, we do not yet have any direct knowledge about large-scale atmospheric motions. There is little to suggest that Uranus (and indeed Neptune) have a banded appearance. The historical observations discussed in Alexander's book are difficult to substantiate.

The most exciting developments have been those made by Smith from the CCD images of the outer planets in the deep methane band of 890 nm (see, for example, Figure 2), which have shown some structure in the upper haze layers and evidence of a bright limb. There are no major discrete features seen yet, which means that there is still some difficulty in prescribing the rotational period of the planet. At the present time, the rotation period is estimated to be 16.31 ± 0.27 hours, but strictly the value probably lies in the range of 15-17 hours. This basic physical characteristic of the planet will be resolved when we can observe both the rotational properties of the magnetosphere to give the solid body rotational period (SYSTEM III), and the motions of any visible cloud systems.

The absence of any significant internal heat source for Uranus will mean that the atmospheric motions will be driven by differential solar heating, even though the Sun's energy will be extremely weak at this distance. The basic properties which govern planetary weather systems are given in Table 2, and it is apparant that Uranus (and Neptune) with their extremely long-time constants, are in a class of their own. The long radiative time constants compared with the length of the Uranian day would suggest a relatively more stable atmosphere than the others in our Solar

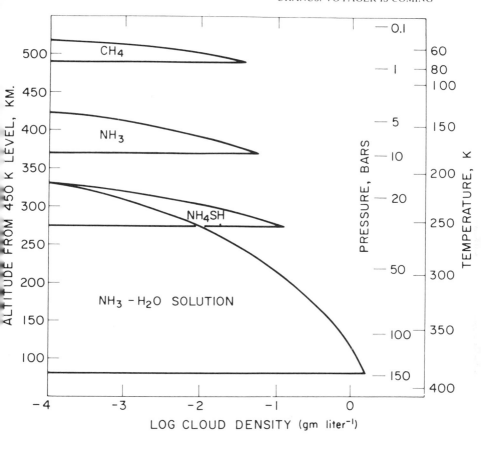

Figure 1. A possible atmospheric and cloud structure model of Uranus. The ice-forming volatiles H_0, NH. CH4, and the rock-forming volatile H_S are assumed to be enhanced by a factor of 10 above solar composition relative to Hydrogen and Helium (after Weidenschilling and Lewis 'Icarus' 20 465–473 (1973)).

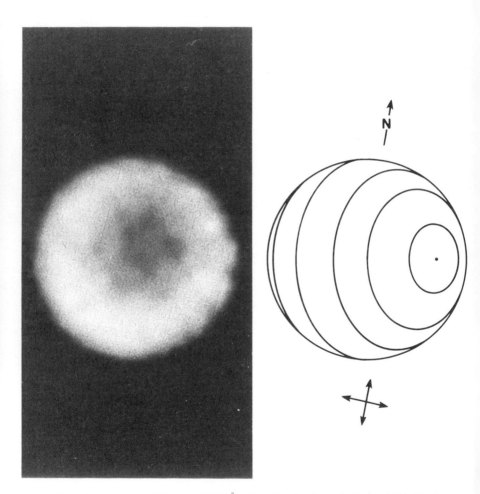

Figure 2. An image of Uranus at 8900 Å obtained by Professor B. A. Smith (University of Arizona).

TABLE 2

Basic Properties of Planetary Atmospheres

	Albedo	Effective Temp (K)	Measured Temp (K)	Adiabatic Lapse Rate (°K/Km)	Radiative Time Constant
Earth	0.3	256	256	~ 9.8	60 days
Jupiter	0.33 ± 0.02	106	124.9 ± 0.3	1.9	~ 6 yrs
Saturn	0.343 ± 0.032	76 ± 4	95.0 ± 0.4	0.9	~ 6 yrs
Uranus	0.34 – 0.5	55 – 58	58 ± 2	~ 1.0	~ 600 yrs
Neptune	0.34 – 0.5	43 – 46	~ 55	± 1.4	± 2200 yrs

System. The large inclination of the axis of rotation will mean that each hemisphere will spend a substantial period without sunlight, The north pole is currently turning towards the Earth and receiving sunlight after an absence of more than forty years, so there will be some meridional heat transport in the atmosphere between pole and equator.

Although we have yet to observe discrete cloud features in the atmosphere of Uranus, our experience with past space mission encounters has taught us to expect surprises, and I anticipate a considerable amount of small-scale detail when we see the planet close up for the first time in early 1986.

2.4 Satellites

Uranus and its satellites resemble some of the properties of the Saturnian system. The five satellites Miranda, Ariel, Umbriel, Titania, and Oberon travel in approximately circular orbits in the plane of the planet's equator. Consequently, whatever was responsible for the tilting of Uranus into its current position probably occurred before the satellite system was developed.

In table 3 we have listed the basic properties of the satellites, which are still no more than tiny points of light in our best telescopes. The current observations suggest that these satellites have water-ice surfaces of varying degrees of purity. Ariel, Umbriel, Titania, and Oberon have opposition surges of greater than 0.5 mag, which are the largest known over 3° of solar phase

TABLE 3

Some Properties of the Satellites of Uranus

	Mean Distance from Uranus (km)	Radius (km)	Mass (10^{23} g)	Density (g cm^{-3})
Miranda	130,500	250 ± 110	1.7 ± 1.7	~ 3
Ariel	191,800	665 ± 65	15.6 ± 3.5	1.3 ± 0.5
Umbriel	267,200	555 ± 50	10.0 ± 4.2	1.4 ± 0.6
Titania	438,000	800 ± 60	59.0 ± 7.0	2.7 ± 0.6
Titania (Co-orbital)	≈ 438,000	~ 250	?	?
Oberon	586,300	815 ± 70	60.0 ± 7.0	2.6 ± 0.6

angle. These objects also seem to have low albedos relative to those typical of pure, heavily gardened water-ice surfaces. There is a spectrally neutral component on the surfaces of Ariel, Umbriel, Titania, and Oberon, which has spectral characteristics similar to carbon black, charcoal, carbonaceous chondritic material and other neutrally coloured, low reflectance material.

There is no evidence yet that volatiles such as methane and carbon monoxide exist on the surfaces of any of these bodies, although there are unidentified features in the spectra of Ariel.

The Uranian satellites are comparable in size to the largest of Saturn's icy satellites. If the apparant increase in satellite density with distance from Uranus is real, this may suggest that it results from catastrophic events that were responsible for the axial orientation for the entire Uranian system.

It is now thought that Titania has a co-orbital satellite and it is quite likely that more such satellites, and tiny bodies amongst the rings, will be discovered during the Voyager encounter. The similarities with and the differences from Saturn will be an interesting aspect of the exploration of the Uranian environment.

2.5 Rings

The current knowledge of the rings of Uranus have been derived from observations of thirteen stellar occultations since 1977. These data have a limiting sensitivity of a few hundredths in optical depth and can resolve structural features separated by 3.5 km. The location of a ring feature can be established with a precision of about 0.1 km.

These observations show that there are nine rings extending from 1.6 to 1.96 Rυ and named in order of increasing distance from Uranus, they are labelled 6, 5, 4, α, β, η, γ, δ, ε. In Table 4 we have compared the major features of the rings of Jupiter, Saturn, and Uranus, and although a ring has now been detected around Neptune, there is no quantitative information yet available to describe it.

TABLE 4

Some Properties of the Rings of Uranus

Feature	Distance (km)	Eccen.	Incl.
6	41,880	0.0010	0.066
5	42,280	0.0018	0.050
4	42,610	0.0012	0.022
α	44,760	0.0008	0.017
β	45,700	0.0004	0.006
η	47,210	~ 0	~ 0.003
γ	47,670	~ 0	~ 0.006
δ	48,340	0.0001	0.012
ε	51,190	0.0079	~ 0.003

The Uranian rings have a circumference of some 250,000 km but they are individually quite narrow. Most are no wider than tens of kilometres, and a few are much narrower. The widest, the ε ring, varies in width from 50 to 100 km.

Rather like the Saturn system, the rings of Uranus are separated by gaps. The boundaries of the rings are sharp which could suggest that there are embedded shepherding satellites, as small as 10 km in diameter, and are therefore undetectable from the Earth. The distribution of rings and gaps may be the result of the gravitational effects of the nearby larger satellites.

A major difference of the Uranian rings from any system yet

detected is their very low reflectivity. The albedo of the material in the rings is estimated at 20 per cent, which is much lower than the usual icy material we expect to find in the outer Solar System. However, the suggestion that the satellites may have very dark material on their surfaces raises the possibility that the dark ring material has been eroded from disrupted satellites. There is clearly a great deal still to learn about this distant part of the Solar System (Figure 3).

3. The Voyager Encounter

On August 20th, 1977 the Voyager 2 spacecraft was launched from Cape Canaveral on its amazing tour of the outer planets. The journey has already taken the spacecraft past Jupiter and Saturn where, in conjunction with the sister craft Voyager 1, an amazing set of discoveries have been made. Now, after a journey time of eight years, Voyager 2 is rapidly approaching the next landmark encounter with Uranus on January 24th, 1986. It is apparent from

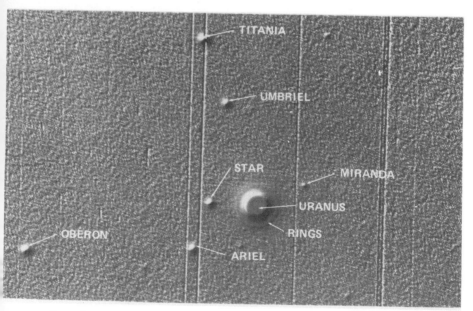

Figure 3. A CCD image of the Uranian system obtained by Professor B. A. Smith (University of Arizona) and Dr R. J. Terrill (JPL).

the previous discussions that there is so much to learn about Uranus that we can expect another 'Voyager spectacular'.

There are some problems that must be faced in preparing for this encounter. The spacecraft is beginning to show signs of wear after these years of virtually continuous operations. At the beginning of the mission one of the receivers on the spacecraft failed, so there is only one in working condition. The system that Voyager relies on contains a failed capacitor which means that the receiver cannot lock on to the frequencies of the signal transmitted from Earth. Consequently, the ground transmitter must send the precise frequency that the receiver is tuned to, and this is extremely sensitive. However, the engineers have now developed techniques that can overcome this situation and have remained in contact with our distant explorer.

The other major problem involves the mechanism that controls the operation of the scan platform which contains the set of remote-sensing instruments, including the camera system. It was this system that malfunctioned during the Saturn encounter and caused the loss of a number of important observations. Extensive tests have been made with the flight spare hardware, and Voyager 1 now moving out of the Solar System. The knowledge gained has enabled a variety of strategies to be implemented into the flight operations. At these immense distances, the light levels are very low, so that much longer exposures are required. Consequently, any motion of the spacecraft will produce the equivalent of 'camera shake'. Some of the exposures may be as long as 10-15 seconds, so that the spacecraft motions could produce a considerable amount of smear in the images. However, Voyager has been constructed with special systems to prevent unnecessary motions, while special software have been constructed to remove the smear from the images. A further major development has been the use of data compression techniques that will enable more data to be transmitted to the Earth than would otherwise be possible at only half the rate available at Saturn. Clearly, the engineers have done all that is possible for the scientists in preparation for the next major planetary encounter.

We can look forward to the prospect of the first detailed investigation of the Uranian system; the investigation of the atmosphere, satellites, and rings. In Figure 4 we illustrate the views of Uranus from the spacecraft, both before and after the encounter. It is expected that some parts of Miranda, the closest viewed satellite, will be observed at a resolution of about 1 km. With the prospect of more than 400 images a day during the mission, with the data from the other sets of instruments, suddenly the veils of secrecy will be lifted from Uranus. But all is not over for Voyager 2; for it now goes on to Neptune in August 1989!

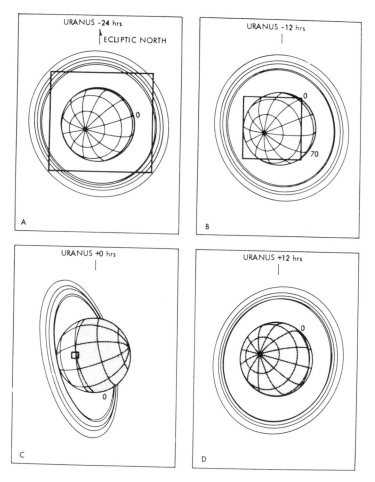

Figure 4. Views of Uranus from the spacecraft at 12 hourly intervals. The square overlay indicates the wide-angle field of view which is 800 picture elements on a side.

4. Some useful References

Alexander, A. F. O'D., *Uranus*, Faber and Faber (1965).

Hunt, G. E., (Ed.), *Uranus and Outer Planets*, C.U.P. (1982).

Hunt, G. E., (Ed.), *Planetary Meteorology*, C.U.P. (1985).

Jones, B. W., *The Solar System*, Pergamon Press (1984).

Lewis, J. S. and Prinn, R. G., *Planets and their Atmospheres*, Academic Press (1984).

Moore, P. and Hunt, G. E., *Atlas of the Solar System*, Mitchell Beazley (1983).

PART THREE

Miscellaneous

Some Interesting Telescopic Variable Stars

Star	R.A.		Dec.			Period,		Remarks
	h	*m*	°		*Mag. range*	*days*	
R. Andromedæ	0	22	+38	18	6.1–14.9	409	
W Andromedæ	2	14	+44	4	6.7–14.5	397	
Theta Apodis	14	00	−76	33	6.4–8.6	119	Semi-regular.
R Aquilæ	19	4	+8	9	5.7–12.0	300	
R Arietis	2	13	+24	50	7.5–13.7	189	
R Aræ	16	35	−56	54	5.9–6.9	4	Algol type.
R Aurigæ	5	13	+53	32	6.7–13.7	459	
R Boötis	14	35	+26	57	6.7–12.8	223	
Eta Carinæ	10	43	−59	25	−0.8–7.9	—	Unique erratic variable.
I Carinæ	09	43	−62	34	3.9–10.0	381	
R Cassiopeiæ	23	56	+51	6	5.5–13.0	431	
T Cassiopeiæ	0	20	+55	31	7.3–12.4	445	
X Centauri	11	46	−41	28	7.0–13.9	315	
T Centauri	13	38	−33	21	5.5–9.0	91	Semi-regular.
T Cephei	21	9	+68	17	5.4–11.0	390	
R Crucis	12	20	−61	21	6.9–8.0	5	Cepheid.
Omicron Ceti	2	17	−3	12	2.0–10.1	331	Mira.
R Coronæ Borealis	15	46	+28	18	5.8–14.8	—	Irregular
W Coronæ Borealis	16	16	+37	55	7.8–14.3	238	
R Cygni	19	35	+50	5	6.5–14.2	426	
U Cygni	20	18	+47	44	6.7–11.4	465	
W Cygni	21	34	+45	9	5.0–7.6	131	
SS Cygni	21	41	+43	21	8.2–12.1	—	Irregular.
Chi Cygni	19	49	+32	47	3.3–14.2	407	Near Eta.
Beta Doradûs	05	33	−62	31	4.5–5.7	9	Cepheid.
R Draconis	16	32	+66	52	6.9–13.0	246	
R Geminorum	7	4	+22	47	6.0–14.0	370	
U Geminorum	7	52	+22	8	8.8–14.4	—	Irregular.
R Gruis	21	45	−47	09	7.4–14.9	333	
S Gruis	22	23	−48	41	6.0–15.0	410	
S Herculis	16	50	+15	2	7.0–13.8	307	
U Herculis	16	23	+19	0	7.0–13.4	406	
R Hydræ	13	27	−23	1	4.0–10.0	386	
R Leonis	9	45	+11	40	5.4–10.5	313	Near 18, 19.
X Leonis	9	48	+12	7	12.0–15.1	—	Irregular (U Gem type).
R Leporis	4	57	−14	53	5.9–10.5	432	'Crimson star.'
R Lyncis	6	57	+55	24	7.2–14.0	379	
W Lyræ	18	13	+36	39	7.9–13.0	196	

Star	R.A.		Dec.		Mag. range	Period days	Remarks
	h	m	°	'			
T Normæ	15	40	−54	50	6.2–13.4	293	
HR Delphini	20	40	+18	58	3.6–?	–	Nova, 1967.
S Octantis	17	46	−85	48	7.4–14.0	259	
U Orionis	5	53	+20	10	5.3–12.6	372	
Kappa Pavonis	18	51	−67	18	4.0–5.5	9	Cepheid.
R Pegasi	23	4	+10	16	7.1–13.8	378	
S Persei	2	19	+58	22	7.9–11.1	810	Semi-regular.
R Sculptoris	01	24	−32	48	5.8–7.7	363	Semi-regular.
R Phœnicis	23	53	−50	05	7.5–14.4	268	
Zeta Phœnicis	01	06	−55	31	3.6–4.1	1	Algol type.
R Pictoris	04	44	−49	20	6.7–10.0	171	Semi-regular.
L² Puppis	07	12	−44	33	2.6–6.0	141	Semi-regular.
Z Puppis	07	30	−20	33	7.2–14.6	510	
T Pyxidis	09	02	−32	11	7.0–14.0	–	Recurrent nova (1920, 1944)
R Scuti	18	45	−5	46	5.0–8.4	144	
R Serpentis	15	48	+15	17	5.7–14.4	357	
SU Tauri	5	46	+19	3	9.2–16.0	–	Irregular (R CrB type).
R Ursæ Majoris	10	41	+69	2	6.7–13.4	302	
S Ursæ Majoris	12	42	+61	22	7.4–12.3	226	
T Ursæ Majoris	12	34	+59	46	6.6–13.4	257	
S Virginis	13	30	−6	56	6.3–13.2	380	
R Vulpeculæ	21	2	+23	38	8.1–12.6	137	

Note: Unless otherwise stated, all these variables are of the Mira type.

Some Interesting Double Stars

We are very grateful to Robert Argyle for this revised list of double stars, which is up to date.

Name	Magnitudes	Separation "	Position angle °	Remarks
Gamma Andromedæ	3.0, 5.0	9.4	064	Yellow, blue. B is again double (0".5) but needs larger telescope.
Zeta Aquarii	4.4, 4.6	1.8	217	Becoming more difficult.
Gamma Arietis	4.2, 4.4	7.8	000	Very easy.
Theta Aurigæ	2.7, 7.2	3.5	313	Stiff test for 3"0G.
Delta Boötis	3.2, 7.4	105	079	Fixed.
Epsilon Boötis	3.0, 6.3	2.8	335	Yellow, blue. Fine pair.
Kappa Boötis	5.1, 7.2	13.6	237	Easy.
Zeta Cancri	5.6, 6.1	5.6	085	Again double.
Iota Cancri	4.4, 6.5	31	307	Easy. Yellow, blue.
Alpha Canum Ven.	3.2, 5.7	19.6	228	Easy. Yellowish, bluish.
Alpha Capricorni	3.3, 4.2	376	291	Naked-eye pair.
Eta Cassiopeiæ	3.7, 7.4	12.2	310	Easy. Creamy, bluish.
Beta Cephei	3.3, 8.0	14	250	Easy with a 3 in.
Delta Cephei	var, 7.5	41	192	Very easy.
Alpha Centauri	0.0, 1.7	21.7	212	Very easy. Binary, period 80 years.
Xi Cephei	4.7, 6.5	6.3	270	Reasonably easy.
Gamma Ceti	3.7, 6.2	2.9	294	Not too easy.
Alpha Circini	3.4, 8.8	15.7	230	PA slowly decreasing.
Zeta Coronæ Bor	4.0, 4.9	6.3	305	PA slowly increasing.
Delta Corvi	3.0, 8.5	24	214	Easy with 3 in.
Alpha Crucis	1.6, 2.1	4.7	114	Third star in low-power field.
Gamma Crucis	1.6, 6.7	111	212	Wide optical pair.
Beta Cygni	3.0, 5.3	34.3	055	Glorious. Yellow, blue.
61 Cygni	5.3, 5.9	29	147	Slowly widening. (Add .5)
Gamma Delphini	4.0, 5.0	9.6	268	Easy. Yellow, greenish.
Nu Draconis	4.6, 4.6	62	312	Naked-eye pair.
Alpha Geminorum	2.0, 2.8	2.6	085	Becoming easier.
Delta Geminorum	3.2, 8.2	6.5	120	Not too easy.

Name	Magnitudes	Separation "	Position angle °	Remarks
Alpha Herculis	var, 6.1	4.6	106	Red, green.
Delta Herculis	3.0, 7.5	8.6	262	Optical pair.
Zeta Herculis	3.0, 6.5	1.5	110	Fine, rapid binary (34y)
Gamma Leonis	2.6, 3.8	4.4	123	Binary; 619 years.
Alpha Lyræ	0.0, 10.5	73	180	Optical. B is faint.
Epsilon Lyræ	4.6, 6.3	2.6	356	Quadruple. Both pairs.
	4.9, 5.2	2.2	093	separable with 3 in.
Zeta Lyræ	4.2, 5.5	44	149	Fixed. Easy double.
Beta Orionis	0.1, 6.7	9.5	205	Can be split with 3 in.
Iota Orionis	3.2, 7.3	11.8	141	Enmeshed in nebulosity.
Theta Orionis	6.8, 7.9	8.7	032	Trapezium in M. 42.
	6.8, 5.4	13.4	241	
Sigma Orionis	4.0, 10.3	11.1	236	Quadruple. C is rather
	6.8, 8.0	30.1	231	faint in small apertures.
Zeta Orionis	2.0, 4.2	2.4	162	Can be split with 3 in.
Eta Persei	4.0, 8.5	28.5	300	Yellow, bluish.
Beta Phœnicis	4.1, 4.1	1.1	319	Slowly closing.
Beta Piscis Austr.	4.4, 7.9	30.4	172	Optical pair. Fixed.
Alpha Piscium	4.3, 5.3	1.9	283	Binary; 720 years.
Kappa Puppis	4.5, 4.6	9.8	318	Again double.
Alpha Scorpii	0.9, 6.8	3.0	275	Red, green.
Nu Scorpii	4.2, 6.5	42	336	Both again double.
Theta Serpentis	4.1, 4.1	22.3	103	Very easy.
Alpha Tauri	0.8, 11.2	131	032	Wide, but B very faint in small telescopes.
Beta Tucanæ	4.5, 4.5	27.1	170	Both again double.
Zeta Ursæ Majoris	2.1, 4.2	14.4	151	Very easy. Naked-eye pair with Alcor.
Alpha Ursæ Minoris	2.0, 9.0	18.3	217	Can be seen with 3 in.
Gamma Virginis	3.6, 3.7	3.5	292	Binary; 171 years. Closing.
Theta Virginis	4.0, 9.0	7.1	343	Not too easy.
Gamma Volantis	3.9, 5.8	13.8	299	Very slow binary.

Some Interesting Nebulæ and Clusters

Object	R.A.		Dec.		Remarks
	h	m	°		
M.31 Andromedæ	00	40.7	+41	05	Great Galaxy, visible to naked eye.
H.VIII 78 Cassiopeiæ	00	41.3	+61	36	Fine cluster, between Gamma and Kappa Cassiopeiæ.
M.33 Trianguli	01	31.8	+30	28	Spiral. Difficult with small apertures.
H.VI 33 4 Persei	02	18.3	+56	59	Double cluster; Sword-handle.
△142 Doradûs	05	39.1	−69	09	Looped nebula round 30 Doradûs. Naked-eye. In Large Cloud of Magellan.
M.1 Tauri	05	32.3	+22	00	Crab Nebula, near Zeta Tauri.
M.42 Orionis	05	33.4	−05	24	Great Nebula. Contains the famous Trapezium, Theta Orionis.
M.35 Geminorum	06	06.5	+24	21	Open cluster near Eta Geminorum.
H.VII 2 Monocerotis	06	30.7	+04	53	Open cluster, just visible to naked eye.
M.41 Canis Majoris	06	45.5	−20	42	Open cluster, just visible to naked eye.
M.47 Puppis	07	34.3	−14	22	Mag. 5,2. Loose cluster.
H.IV 64 Puppis	07	39.6	−18	05	Bright planetary in rich neighbourhood.
M.46 Puppis	07	39.5	−14	42	Open cluster.
M.44 Cancri	08	38	+20	07	Præsepe. Open cluster near Delta Cancri. Visible to naked eye.
M.97 Ursæ Majoris	11	12.6	+55	13	Owl Nebula, diameter 3'. Planetary.
Kappa Crucis	12	50.7	−60	05	"Jewel Box"; open cluster, with stars of contrasting colours.
M.3 Can. Ven.	13	40.6	+28	34	Bright globular.
Omega Centauri	13	23.7	−47	03	Finest of all globulars. Easy with naked eye.
M.80 Scorpii	16	14.9	−22	53	Globular, between Antares and Beta Scorpionis.
M.4 Scorpii	16	21.5	−26	26	Open cluster close to Antares.
M.13 Herculis	16	40	+36	31	Globular. Just visible to naked eye.
M.92 Herculis	17	16.1	+43	11	Globular. Between Iota and Eta Herculis.
M.6 Scorpii	17	36.8	−32	11	Open cluster; naked-eye.
M.7 Scorpii	17	50.6	−34	48	Very bright open cluster; naked eye.
M.23 Sagittarii	17	54.8	−19	01	Open cluster nearly 50' in diameter.
H.IV 37 Draconis	17	58.6	+66	38	Bright Planetary.
M.8 Sagittarii	18	01.4	−24	23	Lagoon Nebula. Gaseous. Just visible with naked eye.
NGC 6572 Ophiuchi	18	10.9	+06	50	Bright planetary, between Beta Ophiuchi and Zeta Aquilæ.
M.17 Sagittarii	18	18.8	−16	12	Omega Nebula. Gaseous. Large and bright.
M.11 Scuti	18	49.0	−06	19	Wild Duck. Bright open cluster.
•M.57 Lyræ	18	52.6	+32	59	Ring Nebula. Brightest of planetaries.
M.27 Vulpeculæ	19	58.1	+22	37	Dumb-bell Nebula, near Gamma Sagittæ.
H.IV 1 Aquarii	21	02.1	−11	31	Bright planetary near Nu Aquarii.
M.15 Pegasi	21	28.3	+12	01	Bright globular, near Epsilon Pegasi.
M.39 Cygni	21	31.0	+48	17	Open cluster between Deneb and Alpha Lacertæ. Well seen with low powers.

Our Contributors

Dr David Allen needs no introduction to readers of the *Yearbook:* no issue would be complete without him. He continues his work at Siding Spring, and is busy on many research programmes.

Dr Fiona Vincent is a graduate of St Andrews University, and while there carried out research into the orbits of minor planets. She is now Director of the Mills Observatory in Dundee.

Dr John Davies is carrying out his researches at the University of Birmingham. He was one of the main workers on the IRAS programme, which involved many new discoveries.

Eric Strach, an orthopaedic surgeon by profession, is a keen astronomer; a former President of the Liverpool Astronomical Society; has observed the Sun regularly for fifteen years; and has studied Hydrogen alpha phenomena for the past ten years.

Dr Alan E. Wright is a Principal Research Scientist at the Australian National Radio Observatory at Parkes, operated by CSIRO.

Dr David L. Block is Lecturer in charge of the Astronomy Course at the University of the Witwatersrand, Johannesburg. After obtaining his BSc (Honours) degree in Applied Mathematics, he completed his MSc degree in Relativity, and his doctorate dealt with galaxies.

Dr Garry E. Hunt Director of the Centre for Remote Sensing and Head of Atmospheric Physics at Imperial College of Science and Technology, University of London, and an experimenter on a number of NASA space missions, including Voyager, Viking and the Earth Radiation Budget Experiment. Received NASA awards and the Gaskell Memorial Medal of the Royal Meteorological Society for his planetary research. Published seven books on planetary and meteorological topics and more than two hundred research papers. Current President of the International Commission on Planetary Atmospheres and their Evolution (IAMAP) and Vice President of Commission 16, 'The Planets' of the International Astronomical Union.

Andrew Hollis is a chartered engineer living in Cheshire. He has been a member of the BBA since 1961 and directs the new Minor Planets Section. As an active member of the IAPPP, he is encouraging amateurs in the UK to take up photoelectric photometry.

Astronomical Societies in Great Britain

The advantages of joining an astronomical society are obvious enough. Full information about national and local Societies was given in the 1966 *Yearbook*; a condensed list, suitably brought up to date, is given below. *Editor's Note.* It has been decided to omit subscriptions as they were found to be continually out of date.

British Astronomical Association
Secretary: E. Watson-Jones, Burlington House, Piccadilly, London, W1.
Meetings: Lecture Hall of Scientific Societies, Civil Service Commission Building, 23 Savile Row, London W1. Last Wednesday each month (Oct.–June), 1700 hrs and some Saturday afternoons.

Association for Astronomy Education
Secretary: Capt. P. Richards-Jones, Crosstrees, 9 Old Oak Avenue, Chipstead, Coulsdon, Surrey.
Meetings: Annually.

Astronomical Society of Wales
Secretary: Clyde Morris, 173 Hanover Street, Swansea, Glamorgan.

Federation of Astronomical Societies
Secretary: D. Powell, 1 Tal-y-bont Road, Ely, Cardiff, South Wales.

Irish Astronomical Association
Secretary: N. Whyte, The Planetarium, College Hill, Armagh.
Meetings: The Ashby Institute, Stanmillis Road, Belfast, fortnightly.

Junior Astronomical Society
Secretary: Martin Ratcliffe, 36 Sandown Way, Greenham, Newbury, Berkshire.
Meetings: Central Library, Theobalds Road, London WC1. Last Saturday Jan., April, July, Oct. 2.30 p.m.

Aberdeen and District Astronomical Society
Secretary: Alex Thompson, Craiglag Cottage, Durris, Banchory,, Aberdeen.
Meetings: Robert Gordon's Institute of Technology, St Andrew's Street, Aberdeen, Friday 7.30 p.m.

Altrincham and District Astronomical Society
Secretary: Colin Henshaw, 10 Delamore Road, Gatley, Cheadle, Cheshire.
Meetings: Park Road Library, Timperley. 1st Friday of each month, 7.30 p.m.

Astra Astronomy Section
Secretary: Ian Downie, 151 Sword Street, Glasgow, G31.
Meetings: Public Library, Airdrie. Weekly.

Aylesbury Astronomical Society
Secretary: N. Neale, 9 Elm Close, Butler's Cross, Aylesbury.
Meetings: As arranged.

Bassettlaw Astronomical Society
Secretary: P. R. Stanley, 28 Festival Avenue, Harworth, nr. Doncaster.
Meetings: Farr, Community Hall, Chapel Walk, Westgate, Worksop, Notts. Tuesday fortnightly, 7.30 p.m.

Bideford Astronomical Society
Secretary: David Lemon, 5 Capern Road, Bideford, N. Devon
Meetings: Torridge Inn, Torridge Hill. Last Monday in Month Sept.–May. 7.15 p.m.

Birmingham Astronomical Society
Secretary: P. Truelove, 58 Taylor Road, King's Heath, Birmingham.
Meetings: Room 261, University of Aston, last Tuesday each month, Sept. to May.

Bolton Astronomical Society
Secretary: Peter Miskiw, 9 Hedley Street, Bolton.

Border Astronomical Society
Secretary: David Pettit, 14 Shap Grove, Carlisle, Cumbria.

Boston Astronomers
Secretary: B. Tongue, South View, Fen Road, Stickford, Boston.
Meetings: Details from the Secretary.

Bradford Astronomical Society
Secretary: B. Jones, 28 High House Avenue, Bolton, Bradford, W. Yorks.
Meetings: Eccleshill Library, Bradford 2. Monday fortnightly (with occasional variations).
Braintree, Halstead & District Astronomical Society
Chairman: A. W. Gatward, 19 Belle Vue Terrace, Halstead. Essex.
Bridgend Amateur Astronomical Society
Secretary: J. M. Pugsley, 32 Hoel Fawr, Broadlands, North Cornelly, Bridgend.
Meetings: G.P. Room,Recreation Centre, Bridgend, 1st and 3rd Friday each month, 7.30 p.m.
Bridgwater Astronomical Society
Secretary: W. L. Buckland, The Bridgwater College, Broadway, Bridgwater, Somerset.
Meetings: The Art Centre, Castle St, Bridgwater. 2nd Wednesday each month, 7.30 p.m.
Brighton Astronomical Society
Secretary: Mrs B. C. Smith, Flat 2, 23 Albany Villas, Hove, Sussex, BN3 2RS.
Meetings: Preston Tennis Club, Preston Drive, Brighton. Weekly, Tuesdays.
Bristol Astronomical Society
Secretary: P. Aughton, 33A Coombe Lane, Bristol.
Meetings: Royal Fort (Rm G44), Bristol University. Every Friday each month, Sept.–May. Fortnightly, June–August.
Cambridge Astronomical Association
Secretary: Mrs Carol Madden, 23 Scotsdowne Road, Trumpington, Cambridge.
Meetings: The Village College, Comberton, Cambridge. 2nd Mon. each month, 19.30 hrs.
Cardiff Astronomical Society
Secretary: D. W. S. Powell, 1 Tal-y-Bont Road, Ely, Cardiff.
Meeting Place: Room 230, Dept. Law, University College, Museum Avenue, Cardiff. Alternate Thursdays, 8 p.m.
Chelmsford and District Astronomical Society
Secretary: Miss C. C. Puddick, 6 Walpole Walk, Rayleigh, Essex.
Meetings: 7.45 p.m. Sandon House School, Sandon Near Chelmsford. 2nd and last Monday of month.
Chelmsley Astronomical Society
Secretary: J. Williams, 100 Stanway Road, Shirley, Solihull, West Midlands
Meetings: Chelmsley Wood Library. Last Thursday in month.
Chester Astronomical Society
Secretary: R. K. Williams, 54 Windways, Little Sutton, South Wirral.
Meetings: The Bull and Stirrup Hotel, Upper Northgate Street, Chester. Last Tuesday of month except Aug. and Dec.
Chester Society of Natural Science, Literature and Art
Secretary: Paul Braid, 'White Wing', 38 Bryn Avenue, Old Colwyn, Colwyn Bay, Clwyd.
Meetings: Grosvenor Museum, Chester. Fortnightly.
Chesterfield Astronomical Society
Secretary: H. Marsh, The Highlands, Chander Hill Lane, Holymoorside, Chesterfield.
Meetings: Barnett Observatory, Newbold. Each Friday.
Clacton & District Astronomical Association
Secretary: C. L. Haskell, 105 London Road, Clacton-on-Sea, Essex.
Cleethorpes & District Astronomical Society
Secretary: P. H. Rea, 81 Freeston St, Cleethorpes, South Humberside, DN35 7PA.
Meetings: Beacon Hill Observatory, Cleethorpes. 1st Wednesday each month.
Cleveland Astronomical Society
Secretary: John Nicol, 44 Bradbury Road, Norton, Stockton-on-Tees, Cleveland
Meetings: Monthly.
Colchester Amateur Astronomers
Secretary: F. Kelly, 'Middleton', Church Road, Elmstead Market, Colchester, Essex.
Meetings: William Loveless Hall, High Street, Wivenhoe. Friday evenings. Fortnighly.
Coventry & Warwicks Astronomical Society
Secretary: Alan Hancocks, 33 Gainford Rise, Binley, Coventry.
Meetings: Coventry Technical College. 1st Friday each month, Sept–June.
Crawley Astronomical Society
Secretary: G. Cowley, 67 Climpixy Road, Ifield, Crawley, Sussex.
Meetings: Crawley College of Further Education. Monthly Oct.–June.
Crayford Manor House Astronomical Society
Secretary: R. H. Chambers, Manor House Centre, Crayford, Kent.
Meetings: Manor House Centre, Crayford. Monthly during term-time.

Croydon Astronomical Society
Secretary: Mrs V. Morgan-Jones, 74 Farley Road, South Croydon CR2 7ND.
Meetings: Lanfranc High School, Mitcham Rd., Croydon. Alternate Fridays, 7.45 p.m.

Dartington Astronomical Society
Secretary: Mrs Iris Allison, 'Wayfaring', Cott Lane, Dartington, Totnes, Devon.
Meetings: Meeting Room, Shinners Bridge Centre, Dartington, 3rd Wed. each month at 8 p.m. Observation all other Wed. evenings (weather permitting) on Foxhole clock tower.

Derby & District Astronomical Society
Secretary: Jane D. Kirk, 7 Cromwell Avenue, Findern, Derby.
Meetings: At home of Secretary. First and third Friday each month, 7.30 p.m.

Doncaster Astronomical Society
Secretary: J. A. Day, 297 Lonsdale Avenue, Intake, Doncaster.
Meetings: Fridays, weekly.

Dundee Astronomical Society
Secretary: G. Young, c/o Flood, 48 Byron Street, Dundee.
Meetings: Mills Observatory, Balgay Park, Dundee. First Saturday each month, 7.30 p.m. Sept.–April.

Easington and District Astronomical Society
Secretary: T. Bradley, 52 Jameson Road, Hartlepool, Co. Durham.
Meetings: Easington Comprehensive School, Easington Colliery. Every third Thursday throughout the year, 7.30 p.m.

Eastbourne Astronomical Society
Secretary: R. W. Cripps, 20 Hailsham Road, Polegate, East Sussex.
Meetings: St. Michael's Church Hall, Willingdon Road, Eastbourne. Last Saturday each month (except July and August).

East Lancashire Astronomical Society
Secretary: D. Chadwick, 16 Worston Lane, Great Harwood, Blackburn, BB6 7TH.
Meetings: As arranged. Monthly.

Astronomical Society of Edinburgh
Secretary: R. G. Fenoulhet, 7 Greenend Gardens, Edinburgh, EH17 7QB.
Meetings: City Observatory, Calton Hill, Edinburgh. Monthly.

Edinburgh University Astronomical Society
Secretary: c/o Dept. of Astronomy, Royal Observatory, Blackford Hill, Edinburgh.

Ewell Astronomical Society
Secretary: Ron W. Johnson, 19 Elm Way, Ewell, Surrey.
Meetings: 1st Friday of each month.

Exeter Astronomical Society
Secretary: Miss J. Corey, 5 Egham Avenue, Topsham Road, Exeter.
Meetings: The Meeting Room, Wynards, Magdalen Street, Exeter. 1st Thursday of month.

Farnham Astronomical Society
Secretary: Laurence Anslow, 14 Wellington Lane, Farnham, Surrey.
Meetings: Church House, Union Road, Farnham. 2nd Monday each month, 7.45 p.m.

Furness Astronomical Society
Secretary: B. B. Sylvester, 38 Sanderling Lane, Dalton-in-Furness, Cumbria.
Meetings: Members' homes. 1st Saturday in month, 7.30 p.m. No August meeting.

Fylde Astronomical Society
Secretary: 28 Belvedere Road, Thornton, Lancs.
Meetings: Stanley Hall, Rossendale Ave. South. 1st Wednesday each month.

Astronomical Society of Glasgow
Secretary: H. Palmer, 8 Kirkeswald Road, Newlands, Glasgow.
Meetings: University of Strathclyde, George St, Glasgow. 3rd Thursday each month, Sept.–April.

Guernsey: La Societe Guernesiaise Astronomy Section
Secretary: David Le Conte, 1 Clos de Fosse André, St. Peter Port, Guernsey.
Meetings: Monthly.

Guildford Association Society
Secretary: Mrs Joan Prosser, 115 Farnham Road, Guildford, Surrey.
Meetings: Guildford Institute, Ward Street, Guildford. 1st Thursday each month, Sept.–June, 7.30 p.m.

Gwynedd Astronomical Society
Secretary: Mr R. Stanley, 48 College Road, Bangor, Gwynedd.
Meetings: Physics Lecture Room, Bangor University. 1st Thursday each month, 7.30 p.m.

Astronomical Society of Haringey
Secretary: W. T. Baker, 58 Stirling Road, Wood Green, London, N.22.
Meetings: 673 Lordship Lane, Wood Green, London, N.22. 3rd Thursday each month, 7.30 p.m.

The Hampshire Astronomical Group
Secretary: S. W. Hackman, 52 Denbigh Drive, Fareham, Hampshire.
Meetings: The Group Observatory.

Hebden Bridge Literary & Scientific Society, Astronomical Section
Secretary: F. Parker, 48 Caldene Avenue, Mytholmroyd, Hebden Bridge, West Yorkshire.

Herschel Astronomical Society
Secretary: C. C. Hall, 46 Whittaker Road, Britwell Estate, Slough, Berks.
Meetings: Trinity Church Annex, Windsor Road, Slough. Fortnightly, Friday. Home meetings as arranged.

Huddersfield Astronomical and Philosophical Society
Secretary: P. R. W. Pendred F.I.M.L.S., 75 Greenhead Road, Marsh, Huddersfield, HD1 4EY.

Hull and East Riding Astronomical Society
Secretary: Keith Winn, 12 Chatham Street, Albert Avenue, Hull
Meetings: Department of Law and Social Sciences Building, Hull University, Cottingham Road, Hull. 1st Friday each month, Oct.-April.

Ilkeston & District Astronomical Society
Secretary: Bernard Wheeldon, 89 Heanor Road, Ilkeston.
Meeting: Erewash Museum, Ilkeston. 2nd Tuesday monthly.

Isle of Wight Astronomical Society
Secretary: J. W. Feakins, 1 Hilltop Cottages, High Street, Freshwater, Isle of Wight.
Meetings: Unitarian Church Hall, Newport, Isle of Wight. Monthly.

King's Lynn Amateur Astronomical Association
Secretary: P. Twynman, 17 Poplar Avenue, R.A.F. Marham, King's Lynn.
Meetings: As arranged.

Lancaster and Morecambe Astronomical Society
Secretary: Miss E. Haygarth, 27 Coulston Road, Bowerham, Lancaster.
Meetings: Trades Hall, Fenton Street, Lancaster, Monthly, 1st Thursday, 7.30 p.m. (except July and August).

Lancaster University Astronomical Society
Secretary: c/o Students Union, Alexandra Square, University of Lancaster.
Meetings: As arranged.

Laymans Astronomical Society
Secretary: John Evans, 10 Arkwright Walk, The Meadows, Nottingham.
Meetings: The Popular, Bath Street, Ilkeston, Derbyshire. Monthly.

Leeds Astronomical Society
Secretary: A. J. Higgins, 23 Montagu Place, Leeds, LS8 2RQ.
Meetings: Lecture Room, City Museum Library, The Headrow, Leeds.

Leicester Astronomical Society
Secretary: Dereck Brown, 64 Grange Drive, Glen Parva, Leicester.
Meetings: Judgemeadow Community College, Marydene Drive, Evington, Leicester. 2nd and 4th Tuesdays each month, 7.30 p.m.

Lincoln Astronomical Society
Secretary: T. Hopkinson, 121 Longdales Road, Lincoln.
Meetings: The Lecture Hall, off Westcliffe Street, Lincoln. 1st Tuesday each month.

Liverpool Astronomical Society
Secretary: Martin Sugget
Meetings: City Museum, Liverpool. Monthly

Loughton Astronomical Society
Secretary: S. Smith, 6 Baldock Road, Theydon Bois, Epping, Essex.
Meetings: Loughton Hall, Rectory Lane, Loughton, Essex. Thursdays, 8 p.m.

Lowestoft and Great Yarmouth Regional Astronomers (LYRA) Society
Secretary: S. Briggs, 65 Stubbs Wood, Gunton Park, Lowestoft, Suffolk.
Meetings: Committee Room No. 30, Lowestoft College of F.E., St Peter's Street, Lowestoft, 3rd Thursday, Sept.–May (Weather permitting on Corton Cliff site), 7.15 p.m.

Luton Astronomical Society
Secretary: D. R. White, 54 Barr Street, Dunstable.
Meetings: Luton College of Higher Education, Park Square, Luton. Second and last Friday each month, 7.30 p.m.

Lytham St. Annes Astronomical Association
Secretary: K. J. Porter, 141 Blackpool Road, Ansdell, Lytham St. Annes, Lancs.
Meetings: College of Further Education, Clifton Drive S., Lytham St. Annes. 2nd Wednesday monthly Oct.–June.

Maidenhead Astronomical Society
Secretary: T. V. Haymes, 58 Portlock Road, Maidenhead.
Meetings: Library. Monthly (except July and August. 3rd Tuesday.)

Manchester Astronomical Society
Secretary: J. H. Davidson, Godlee Observatory, U.M.I.S.T., Sackville Street, Manchester 1.
Meetings: At the Observatory, Thursdays, 7.30–9 p.m.

Mansfield and Sutton Astronomical Society
Secretary: A Brooks, 2 East Street, Sutton-in-Ashfield, Notts.
Meetings: Sherwood Observatory, Oakmoor Road. Last Tuesday each month.

Mexborough and Swindon Night Sky Astronomical Society
Secretary: E. Marris, 42 Swaith Avenue, Scawthorpe, Doncaster, DN5 9PB.
Meetings: Methodist Hall, Piccadilly Road, Swinton, Near Mexborough. Thursdays, 7 p.m.

Mid-Kent Astronomical Society
Secretary: Brian A. van de Peep, 11 Berber Road, Strood, Rochester, Kent.
Meetings: Medway Teachers Centre, Vicarage Road, Strood, Rochester, Kent, last Friday in month. Mid Kent College, Horsted, 2nd Friday in month.

Mid Sussex Astronomical Society
Secretary: Dr L. K. Brundle, 63 Pasture Hill Road, Haywards Heath, W. Sussex.
Meetings: Sixth Form College, Harlands Road, Haywards Heath. Monthly, Wednesdays 7.30 p.m.

Milton Keynes Astronomical Society
Secretary: The Secretary, Milton Keynes Astronomical Society, Bradwell Abbey Field Centre, Bradwell, Milton Keynes, MK1 39AP.
Meetings: Alternate Tuesdays.

Newbury Amateur Astronomical Society
Secretary: Mrs A. Davies, 11 Sedgfield Road, Greenham, Newbury, Berks.
Meetings: Waterside Youth Centre, Newbury. Last Friday of month, Aug.–May.

Newcastle-on-Tyne Astronomical Society
Secretary: D. S. Brown, c/o Sir Howard Grubb Parsons & Co. Ltd., Walkergate. Newcastle-on-Tyne, NE6 2YB.
Meetings: Botany Lecture Theatre, Newcastle University. Monthly, Sept.–April.

Newtonian Observatory Astronomical Society
Secretary: Miss P. E. Randle, 62 Northcott Road, Worthing, Sussex.
Meetings: Adult Education Centre, Union Place, Worthing. 1st Wednesday each month except Aug. 7.30 p.m.

North Clwyd Astronomical Society
Secretary: D. S. Owen, 2 Lon Kinmel, Pensarn, Abergele, Clwyd.

North Devon Astronomical Society
Secretary: D. Lemon, 5 Capern Rd, Bideford.
Meetings: Pilton Community College, Chaddiford Lane, Barnstaple. 1st Wednesday each month, Sept.-May.

North Dorset Astronomical Society
Secretary: J. E. M. Coward, The Pharmacy, Stalbridge, Dorset.
Meetings: Charterhay, Stourton, Caundle, Dorset. 2nd Wednesday each month.

North Staffordshire Astronomical Society
Secretary: E. S. Hewitt, 24 Weldon Avenue, Weston Coyney, Stoke-on-Trent.
Meetings: 1st Wednesday of each month at Cartwright House, Broad Street, Hanley.

North Western Association of Variable Star Observers
Secretary: Jeremy Bullivant, 2 Beaminster Road, Heaton Mersey, Stockport, Cheshire, SK4 3HT.
Meetings: Four annually.

North Wilts/South Glos Astronomical Group
Secretary: Simon D. Barnes, 'Kelston', Gloucester Road, Malmesbury, Wilts.
Meetings: To be announced.

Norwich Astronomical Society
Secretary: Miss Lisa Roper, 39 Norwich Road, Poringland, nr. Norwich, NR14 7QR.
Meetings: Colney Lane, Cringleford, Norwich. Every Tuesday, Friday and Saturday night.

Nottingham Astronomical Society
Secretary: C. Brennan, 40 Swindon Close, Giltbrook, Nottingham.
Meetings:

Oldham Astronomical Society
Secretary: P. J. Collins, 25, Park Crescent, Chadderton, Oldham.
Meetings: Werneth Park Study Centre, Frederick Street, Oldham. Fortnightly, Friday.

Open University Astronomical Society
Secretary: Jim Lee, c/o above, Milton Keynes.
Meetings: Open University, Walton Hall, Milton Keynes. As arranged.

Orpington Astronomical Society
Secretary: Mrs June Budd, Caragana, Trotts Lane, Westerham, Kent.
Meetings: Newstead Wood School or Darrick Wood School, 3rd Thursday each month, Oct.–June, 7.30 p.m.

Orwell Astronomical Society (Ipswich)
Secretary: M. A. P. Barriskill, 15 London Road, Ipswich, Suffolk.
Meetings: Orwell Park School, Nacton, Ipswich. Tuesdays, Wednesdays, Saturdays, from 8.00 p.m.

Oxshott Astronomical Society
Secretary: B. J. Donelan, Homelea, Portsmouth Road, Esher, Surrey.
Meetings: Reed's School, Sandy Lane, Cobham, Surrey. Monthly, Sept.–May.

Peterborough Astronomical Society
Secretary: E. Pitchford, 24 Cissbury Ring, Werrington, Peterborough.
Meetings: Peterborough Technical College. 2nd Tuesday, 3rd Thursday each month.

Plymouth Astronomical Society
Secretary: G. S. Pearce, 1 Valletort Cotts, Millbridge, Plymouth.
Meetings: Y.W.C.A., Lockyer Street, Plymouth. Monthly.

Portsmouth Astronomical Society
Secretary: G. B. Bryant, 81 Ringwood Road, Southsea.
Meetings: Monday. Fortnightly.

Preston & District Astronomical Society
Secretary: C. Lynch, 35 Bispham Road, Carleton, Poulton-le-Fylde, Lancs.
Meetings: Chamber of Commerce, 49a Fishergate, Preston. 3rd Monday each month. Sept.–May.

Rayleigh Centre Amateur Astronomical Society
Secretary: Bernard R. Soley, 136 The Chase, Rayleigh, Essex.
Meetings: Fitzwimarc School, Hockley Road, Rayleigh. Every Wednesday, 8 p.m.

Reading Astronomical Society
Secretary: Mrs. Muriel Wrigley, 30 Amherst Road, Reading.
Meetings: St. Peter's Church Hall, Church Road, Earley. Monthly (3rd Sat.), 7–10 p.m.

Renfrew District Astronomical Society (formerly Paisley A.S.)
Secretary: Robert Law. 14d Marmion Court, Forkes, Paisley.

Salford Astronomical Society
Secretary: J. A. Handford, 45 Burnside Avenue, Salford 6, Lancs.
Meetings: The Observatory, Chaseley Road, Salford.

Salisbury Plain Astronomical Society
Secretary: R. J. D. Dias.

Scarborough & District Astronomical Society
Secretary: M. D. Wilson, 19 Ryefield Close, Eastfield, Scarborough, N. Yorks, YO11.
Meetings: North Riding College of Education, Filey Road, Wednesdays, Sept.–June, 7.30–9 p.m.

Sheffield Astronomical Society
Secretary: Mrs Nora Betts, 53 Glen View Road, Sheffield.
Meetings: City Museum, Weston Bank, 3rd Friday each month.

Sidmouth and District Astronomical Society
Secretary: M. Grant, 3 Salters Meadow, Sidmouth, Devon.
Meetings: Norman Lockyer Observatory, Salcombe Hill. 1st Monday in each month.

Solent Amateur Astronomers
Secretary: R. W. Arbour, Pennell Observatory, 29 Wrights Way, South Wonston, Hants.
Meetings: Place to be notified. 3rd Thursday each month, 7.30 p.m.

Southampton Astronomical Society
Secretary: Miss Lilian Hobbs, 64 Wildern Lane, Hedge End, Southampton.
Meetings: Southampton University, 2nd Thursday each month, Sept.–July, 7.30 p.m.

South Downs Astronomical Society
Secretary: Mrs Buss, 32 Birdham Close, Stroud Green, Bognor Regis, West Sussex.
Meetings: Last Friday in each month.

South-East Essex Astronomical Society
Secretary: M. Purser, 64 Goshawk Drive, Chelmsford.
Meetings: Lecture Theatre, Central Library, Victoria Avenue, Southend-on-Sea. Generally 1st Thursday in month, Sept.-May.

South-East Kent Astronomical Society
Secretary: P. Andrew, 30 Reach Close, St Margaret's Bay, nr. Dover.
Meetings: Monthly.

Southern Astronomical Society
Secretary: G. T. Elston, 34 Plummer Road, Clapham Park, London SW4 8HH.
Meetings: As arranged.

South Lincolnshire Astronomical & Geophysical Society
Secretary: F. F. Bermingham, 19 Field Close, Gosberton, Spalding, Lincs.
Meetings: South Holland Centre, Spalding. 3rd Thursday each month, 7.30 p.m.

South London Astronomical Society
Chairman: P. Bruce, 2 Constance Road, West Croydon, CR0 2RS.
Meetings: Surrey Halls, Birfield Road, Stockwell, London, SW4. 2nd Tuesday each month, 8 p.m.

Southport, Ormskirk and District Astronomical Society
Secretary: J. T. Harrison, 92 Cottage Lane, Ormskirk, Lancs, L39 3NJ.
Meetings: Saturday evenings, monthly as arranged.

South Shields Astronomical Society
Secretary: H. Haysham, Marine and Technical College, St George's Avenue, South Shields, Co. Durham.
Meetings: Marine and Technical College. Each Thursday, 7.30 p.m.

South West Herts Astronomical Society
Secretary: G. J. B. Phillips, 32 Riverford Close, Harpenden, Herts.
Meetings: Royal Masonic School for Girls, Rickmansworth. Last Friday each month, Sept.–May.

Stafford and District Astronomical Society
Secretary: Mrs L. Hodkinson, Beecholme, Francis Green Lane, Penkridge, Staffs.
Meetings: Riverside Centre, Stafford. Every 3rd Thursday, Sept.–May, 7.30 p.m.

Stoke-on-Trent Astronomical Society
Secretary: M. Pace, Sundale, Dunnocksfold Road, Alsager, Stoke.
Meetings: Cartwright House, Broad Street, Hanley. Monthly.

Sussex Astronomical Society
Secretary: Mrs C. G. Sutton, 75 Vale Road, Portslade, Sussex.
Meetings: English Language Centre, Third Avenue, Hove. Every Wednesday, 7.30–9.30 p.m. Sept.–May.

Swansea Astronomical Society
Secretary: G. P. Lacey, 32 Glenbran Road, Birchgrove, Swansea.
Meetings: The Mathematics and Physics Building, Swansea University. Every alternate Monday evening.

Thames Valley Astronomical Group
Secretary: K. J. Pallet, 82a Tennyson Street, South Lambeth, London, SW8 3TH.
Meetings: Irregular.

Thanet Amateur Astronomical Society
Secretary: P. F. Jordan, 85 Crescent Road, Ramsgate.
Meetings: Hilderstone House, Broadstairs, Kent. Monthly.

Todmorden Astronomical Society
Secretary: Eric Lord, Sloterdisk, 15 Mons Road, Todmorden, Lancashire.
Meetings: Monthly at Todmorden College.

Torbay Astronomical Society
Secretary: R. Jones, St Helens, Hermose Road, Teignmouth, Devon.
Meetings: Town Hall, Torquay. 3rd Thursday, Oct.–May.

Vectis Astronomical Society
Secretary: R. M. Hayward, Chester Lodge Hotel, Beachfield Road, Sandown, I.W.
Meetings: 1st Friday each month, Oct.–May, Address as above.

Waltham Forest & District Junior Astronomy Club
Secretary: B. Crawford, 24 Fulbourne Road, Walthamstow, London, E.17.
Meetings: 24 Fulbourne Road, Walthamstow, London, E.17. Fortnighly (Mondays).

Warwickshire Astronomical Society
Secretary: R. D. Wood, 20 Humber Road, Coventry, Warwickshire.
Meetings: 20 Humber Road, Coventry. Each Tuesday.

Webb Society
Secretary: S. J. Hynes, 8 Cormorant Close, Sydney, Crewe, Cheshire.
Meetings: As arranged.

Wellingborough District Astronomical Society
Secretary: R. Simmons, 52 Doddington Road, Wellingborough, Northants.
Meetings: Monthly.

Wessex Astronomical Society
Secretary: Mrs J. Broadbank, 154a Albert Road, Parkstone, Poole, Dorset, BH12 2HA.
Meetings: The Cafe Lounge, Allendale Centre, Wimborne, Dorset. 1st Tuesday of each month (except August).

West of London Astronomical Society
Secretary: A. H. Davis, 49 Beaulieu Drive, Pinner, Middx, HA5 1NB.
Meetings: Monthly, alternately at Hillingdon and North Harrow. 2nd Monday of the month, except August.

West Midland Astronomical Association
Secretary: Miss S. Bundy, 93 Greenridge Road, Handsworth Wood, Birmingham.
Meetings: Dr Johnson House, Bull Street, Birmingham. As arranged.

West Yorkshire Astronomical Society
Secretary: J. A. Roberts, 76 Katrina Grove, Purston, Pontefract, Yorks, WF7 5LW.
Meetings: The Barn, 4 The Butts, Back Northgate, Pontefract. Every Tuesday, 7 p.m.

Widnes Astronomical Society
Secretary: Miss A. Williams, 21 Deansway, Ditton, Widnes.
Meetings: To be arranged.

Wolverhampton Astronomical Society
Secretary: M. Astley, Garwick, 8 Holme Mill, Fordhouses, Wolverhampton.
Meetings: Beckminster Methodist Church Hall, Birches Road, Wolverhampton. Alternate Mondays, Sept.–April.

York Astronomical Society
Secretary: R. S. Waterworth, 46 Ruffa Lane, Pickering, North Yorkshire, YO18 7HN.
Meetings: Physics Dept. York University. Fortnightly, Fridays.

It is possible that this list of local societies may not be quite complete. If any have been omitted, or any details need to be updated, the secretaries concerned are invited to write to the Editor (c/o Messrs Sidgwick & Jackson (Publishers), Ltd, 1 Tavistock Chambers, Bloomsbury Way, London W.C.1), so that relevant notes may be included in the 1987 *Yearbook*.

There is now a permanent public exhibition at the Royal Greenwich Observatory, Herstmonceux Castle, Hailsham, East Sussex. It is open on weekdays between 2 and 5.30 p.m., and on Saturdays, Sundays and public holidays from 10.30 a.m. to 5.30 p.m. The Exhibition covers the fields of modern astronomy, the development of telescopes, the history of the Observatory and of the Castle. There is a tea room (June-September), a souvenir shop, and free parking.

The William Herschel Society maintains the museum now established at 19 New King Street, Bath – the only surviving Herschel house. It also undertakes activities of various kinds. New members would be welcome; those interested are asked to contact Dr L. Hilliard at 2 Lambridge, London Road, Bath.